CONTENTS

FOREWORD *v*

INTRODUCTION *1*

1 ORGANISING THE SITE *5*

Planning the work *5*
Organising the work *7*
Common facilities *7*
Control and supervision *19*
Notifying the site to HSE *20*
Monitoring and reviewing *21*
Place of work requiring inspections *21*
Reporting accidents and work-related diseases *23*

2 CONSTRUCTION WORK: THE ESSENTIALS OF HEALTH AND SAFETY *25*

Introduction *25*

Safe place of work *26*

Working at height *26*
Guard rails and toe boards *27*
Safe working platforms *30*
General access scaffolds *30*
Tower scaffolds *32*
Mobile and suspended access equipment *34*
Ladders *41*
Step-ladders *42*
Protection against falling materials *43*
Demolition, dismantling and structural alteration *43*
Steel erection *45*
Formwork and reinforced concrete work *47*
Roof work *50*
Industrial roofing *52*

Groundwork *54*
Excavations *54*
Underground services *57*

Working in confined spaces *59*

Prevention of drowning *62*

Moving, lifting and handling loads   64
Manual handling   65
Small lifting equipment   66
Hoists   66
Mobile cranes   68

Site vehicles and mobile plant   71

Health hazards   73
Hazardous substances and processes   73
Personal protective equipment   75
Personal hygiene   76
Health surveillance   76
Asbestos   77
Noise   80
Vibration   81

Protective equipment   82
Hard hats   82
Footwear   82
Goggles and safety spectacles   83
Outdoor clothing   83
High visibility clothing   83
Gloves   83

Electricity   84
Overhead power lines   87

Work affecting the public   88

3 HEALTH AND SAFETY MANAGEMENT AND THE LAW   93
The Health and Safety at Work etc Act 1974   93
The Management of Health and Safety at Work Regulations 1999   93
The Construction (Health, Safety and Welfare) Regulations 1996   98
The Construction (Head Protection) Regulations 1989   98
The Provision and Use of Work Equipment Regulations 1998   99
The Lifting Operations and Lifting Equipment Regulations 1998   99
The Construction (Design and Management) Regulations 1994   99
Employees' duties   107
Reporting accidents and work-related diseases   108
Inspectors and the law   109

4 REFERENCES AND FURTHER INFORMATION   111
References   111
HSE offices   116

iv

HEALTH AND SAFETY IN

CONSTRUCTION

HSE BOOKS

ISBN 0 7176 2106 5

FOREWORD

Every year many construction site workers are killed or injured as a result of their work; others suffer ill health, such as dermatitis, occupational deafness or asbestosis. The hazards are not, however, restricted to those working on sites. Children and other members of the public are also killed or injured because construction activities have not been adequately controlled.

The construction industry's performance has shown a steady long-term improvement. However, there is no room for complacency. The rates of death, serious injury and ill health are still unacceptably high and, as far as fatalities are concerned, the beginning of the new millennium saw a significant reversal of that downward trend.

We can so easily believe that accidents will always happen to other people and will never touch us. But unless we all recognise our own vulnerability - and just how vulnerable others can be - then, as a result of decisions we take, construction workers and their families will continue to witness the unnecessary injuries, pain and suffering that so tragically afflict the industry.

In addition, accidents and ill health have a financial cost. The business case for improving performance is absolutely clear.

This publication is aimed at the small contractor but is also applicable to all those involved in construction. It provides help and assistance on how to work safely on most tasks you are likely to encounter. It also helps you identify the main causes of accidents and ill health, and explains how to eliminate hazards and control risks. The guidance is simple but comprehensive. The solutions provided are straightforward and easy to adopt. The book also mentions other HSE guidance providing fuller information on health and safety issues for everyone involved in construction, from clients and designers to contractors, individual workers and safety representatives.

'Revitalising health and safety'

The Government and the Health and Safety Commission (HSC) set targets in July 2000 for improving Great Britain's health and safety performance over a ten-year period.

HSC's Construction Industry Advisory Committee (CONIAC), which includes key stakeholders in the industry, has agreed the construction industry's contribution to those targets. They are challenging and, because of the industry's poor record, rightly exceed those of the Government and HSC.

They are to:
* reduce the incidence rate of fatalities and major injuries by 40% by 2004/5 and 66% by 2009/10;
* reduce the incidence rate of cases of work-related ill health by 20% by 2004/5 and 50% by 2009/10;
* reduce the number of working days lost per 100 000 workers from work-related injury and ill health by 20% by 2004/5 and by 50% by 2009/10.

These targets will only be achieved if everyone involved in the construction industry - from clients and designers to contractors and individual workers - plays their part. Leading industry bodies have prepared action plans designed to bring about the cultural changes which are crucial in meeting these targets, and they have committed themselves to their delivery. Action plans need to be cascaded across and down the industry by trade associations, unions and individual companies.

What you can do

Please read this publication and turn the advice into action. Doing so may well prevent you and other people from becoming victims of accidents or suffering ill health.

Finally, I encourage you to take a further step. Prepare and put into effect your own action plan.

Kevin Myers
HM Chief Inspector of Construction
Chair of the Health and Safety Commission's Construction Industry Advisory Committee

Visit the Working Well Together web site (http://wwt.uk.com) for more information, including help with action plans.

INTRODUCTION

What is this book about?

This book explains the essential tasks for achieving healthy and safe construction sites. It helps the reader to identify hazards and control risks and explains how to plan, organise, control, monitor and review health and safety throughout the life of a project.

Who should read this book?

The book is aimed at everybody involved in construction work, including clients, designers, engineers and surveyors. It will appeal most to:

*   directors and partners running construction businesses;
*   site managers and supervisors running sites;
*   managers and supervisors who work on sites run by other companies; and
*   those doing the construction work, including employees, the self-employed and safety representatives.

For further information on safety representatives see *Safety representatives and safety committees.*[1]

Clients, designers and others who specify construction work may also find the book useful. Clients can use the book to identify the skills and competences contractors need to work safely and without risks to health. Designers, specifiers and planning supervisors can use it to identify the most common risks which contractors have to manage on site. They can then take account of how to design out or reduce these risks when they prepare their designs, specifications and plans.

What sort of construction work does the book cover?

It provides guidance for people who work on all kinds of construction sites, including:

*   general building and construction work;
*   refurbishment work;
*   maintenance and repair work;
*   engineering construction work; and
*   civil engineering work.

How is the book structured?

The book is divided into four sections:

Section 1: Organising the site
This section deals with setting up the site. It covers planning, organising, controlling, monitoring and reviewing the job so that site health and safety is taken into account from the very beginning of the job through to its completion.

Matters considered are those relevant to:

- everyone working on the site (for example, emergency procedures and site welfare); and

- the site as a whole (for example, site boundaries and lighting).

These should be planned before work begins.

Section 2: Construction work: The essentials of health and safety

This section is the main part of the book. It summarises the essential health and safety requirements for developing a safe system of work. It helps the reader to identify health and safety hazards found on many sites and advises on how to control the risks that can arise. The book cannot address every hazard, but it does focus on matters which are the common causes of death, injury and ill health. Advice is given on protecting those who are directly employed to do the work, others working on the site, visitors to the site and members of the public who could be affected.

Section 3: Health and safety management and the law

The law requires health and safety issues to be managed and controlled. This section sets out the most important parts of the law which apply to construction. It explains what needs to be done to ensure health and safety is dealt with effectively, including duties:

- employers have to their employees;
- of anyone in control of construction work;
- everyone at work has to others affected by their work;
- of clients; and
- of designers such as architects, engineers etc.

Section 4: References and further information

This section lists sources of further information about site health and safety, including detailed guidance published by the Health and Safety Commission (HSC) and the Health and Safety Executive (HSE).

What are the most common risks considered in this book?

Accidents

The most frequent causes of accidental death and injury are:

- **Falls:** People fall because access to and from the workplace is not adequate, or the workplace itself is not safe. Advice is given about safe access to, and work at, height. There are four high risk operations where falls are of major concern: Roof work, steel erection, formwork and reinforced concrete work and demolition. These are covered in more detail.

  The importance of providing good access to a safe working place (for example, a platform with toe boards and guard rails), cannot be over-emphasised.

- **Falling material and collapses:** People are struck by material falling from loads being lifted and material which rolls or is kicked off work platforms; others are struck or buried by falling materials when excavations, buildings or structures collapse. Structural collapses can range from walls which fall because their foundations are undermined by nearby excavations to buildings which collapse prematurely during demolition because the structure was either unknowingly weakened or overloaded. Scaffolds collapse because ties are either forgotten or removed too early during striking, or the scaffold is overloaded. Structures under construction, for example steel frames which have not been adequately braced, or formwork which is prematurely loaded, may also collapse.

Guidance is provided on preventing these types of accidents, although extra advice from a structural engineer may also be needed.

- **Electrical accidents:** People suffer electric shock and burns when they use unsafe equipment and when they contact overhead electric lines and buried cables. Guidance is provided on avoiding all these types of accident.

- **Mobile plant:** Construction plant can be heavy. It often operates on ground which is muddy and uneven, and where visibility for the driver is poor. People walking on site are injured or killed by moving vehicles, especially reversing ones. Others, particularly drivers and operators, are killed or injured by overturning vehicles and plant.

  This book gives advice on site transport and work near roads where traffic is a risk to workers and where construction operations are a risk to road traffic and pedestrians.

Ill health

The construction industry has a poor health record. Construction workers are likely to suffer ill health as a result of their work in the industry after exposure to both hazardous substances and harsh working conditions. Ill health can result from exposure to dusts, including asbestos, which causes a range of respiratory diseases and cancer. Exposure to dusts, and also solvents, can cause skin diseases such as dermatitis. Lifting heavy and awkward loads causes back and other injuries. Some injuries can result from a single bad lift, but more commonly long-term injury develops as a result of repeated minor injury due to repeated poor lifting practice. Exposure to high noise levels causes deafness. Vibration leads to a range of problems, including vibration white finger.

Guidance is provided on how to eliminate the hazards or where this cannot be done, reduce the risk.

Why has this book been revised?

This guidance has been revised to reflect changes in legislation since it was first published, and the introduction of new legislation relating to the lifting and use of work equipment.

This new/amended legislation includes:

- The Asbestos (Prohibitions) Regulations 1999 - see pages 77-79
- The Control of Substances Hazardous to Health Regulations 1999 - see page 73
- The Lifting Operations and Lifting Equipment Regulations 1998 - see page 99
- The Management of Health and Safety at Work Regulations (MHSW) Regulations) 1999 - see pages 93-98
- The Provision and Use of Work Equipment Regulations 1998 - see page 99.

The guidance also reflects changes in reporting accidents and work-related diseases under RIDDOR '95 - see page 108.

1: ORGANISING THE SITE

The key to achieving healthy and safe working conditions is to ensure that health and safety issues are planned, organised, controlled, monitored and reviewed.

Everyone controlling site work has health and safety responsibilities. Section 3 of the book sets these out.

Check that working conditions are healthy and safe before work begins and ensure that the proposed work is not going to put others at risk. This requires planning and organisation.

This applies equally to a firm running and managing a small job, or to a subcontractor working at a large site controlled by someone else. Planning has to consider changes to the site as it develops - from welfare arrangements at the set-up, through to snagging work and the dismantling of site huts and hoardings at the end of the contract. The basic requirements apply to all jobs.

The principal contractor, who is appointed under the Construction (Design and Management) Regulations 1994 (CDM) (see page 98), has more formal responsibilities for securing health and safety on site. These are set out in Section 3. Whether or not CDM applies, the principles of successful health and safety management are the same.

PLANNING THE WORK

☐ Gathering as much health and safety information about the project and the proposed site before work begins is important. Information available at tendering should be used so that allowance is made for time and resources to deal with particular problems. Sources of information include:

- the client;

- designers;

- contract documents;

- other contractors at the site;

- specialist contractors and consultants;

- trade and contractor organisations;

- equipment and material suppliers; and

- HSE guidance and British Standards.

☐ Find out about the history of the site and its surroundings. See if there are any unusual features which might affect the work, or how the work will affect others. Pay particular attention to:

- asbestos or other contaminants;

- overhead power lines and underground services;

- unusual ground conditions;

- public rights of way across the site;

- nearby schools, footpaths, roads or railways; and

- other activities going on at the site.

Where CDM applies, much of this information should be found in the pre-construction stage health and safety plan. If there is a plan, make sure it is seen and its contents have been taken into account before tenders are submitted. Where CDM does not apply, gathering information is still important.

☐ When estimating costs and preparing the programme, consider any particular health and safety hazards associated with the work. Make sure suitable allowances have been made in the price. The job will run more smoothly, efficiently and profitably if hazards have been predicted, planned for and controlled from the outset. Having to stop or reschedule work to deal with emergencies wastes time and money.

☐ When materials are bought, or equipment is hired, the supplier has a duty to provide certain health and safety information. Make sure this is obtained and read. For example, it may be necessary to:

- consider using a specialist who is familiar with the necessary precautions;

- carry out an assessment of the risks arising from the use of a hazardous substance and consider using a less harmful substance instead; and

- provide training on the safe use of the material or equipment.

☐ When programmes are prepared, consider if there are any operations which will affect the health or safety of others working at the site. For example:

- think about access to the workplace - which trades will need to go where and when? Arrange the programme to make sure everyone who needs to use the scaffold or other means of access has time to do so. Plan to make sure the access will be safe and suitable for their use.

- timber treatment or site radiography usually has to be done when no one else is on site. The site may have to be left vacant for a few days. Where a specialist contractor is used, check the requirements with them and programme the work well in advance.

☐ Discuss proposed working methods with subcontractors before letting contracts. Find out how they are going to work, what equipment and facilities they are expecting to be provided and the equipment they will bring to the site. Identify any health or safety risks which their operations may create for others working at the site and agree control measures. Obtaining health and safety method statements and risk assessments (see pages 95-96) will help. Health and safety method statements with plenty of diagrams are generally most easily understood.

☐ Decide what plant will be required and check that it will be suitable.

☐ Plan material deliveries and consider storage needs.

ORGANISING THE WORK

☐ Decide who will supervise the work - check that they are adequately trained and experienced.

☐ When taking on workers, ask about the training they have received and ask for certificates of training achievement. Get them to demonstrate their knowledge or to show examples of safe working practice before setting them to work.

☐ Make sure that firms coming onto site provide adequate supervision for their workers. Agree what training they will have received or will be provided at the site.

☐ See that work methods and safety precautions agreed before work is started are put into practice. Make sure everyone understands how work is to be done and is aware of relevant method statements before work starts.

☐ Find out if any of the work will be further subcontracted. Make sure that people working for subcontractors also get the information they require and provide training, supervision, etc as needed.

COMMON FACILITIES

Site access

There should be safe access onto and around the site for people and vehicles. Plan how vehicles will be kept clear of pedestrians, especially at site entrances, vehicle loading/unloading areas, parking and manoeuvring places and where driver's vision may be obstructed. For further information, see *The safe use of vehicles on construction sites*.[2]

Site boundaries

Construction work should be fenced off and suitably signed. This will protect people (especially children) from site dangers and the site from vandalism and theft. For some jobs the workplace will have to be shared. Perhaps the work will be done in an operating factory or office. Agree who has to control each area. Agree what fences, barriers, means of separation or permits-to-work are required to keep both construction workers away from hazards created by others and other people away from hazards created by the construction work; site rules might be needed (see page 18). Make sure there is a system to ensure necessary precautions are kept in place during working hours and that night-time and weekend protection is put in place as required before the site closes. For further information, see *Protecting the public - your next move.*[3]

Falling materials

Toe boards must be provided to working platforms to stop materials being kicked, or rolling off platforms. Fans, netting, hoardings or protected walkways may also be needed to protect workers, site visitors and the public where there is particular risk from falling materials. Some processes such as demolition and cutting operations may throw materials out from the work area. Again, fans, hoardings, covered walkways etc may be needed to protect against this risk. (Also see page 88.) Make sure there is a system to maintain necessary protection.

Welfare facilities

Everyone who works on site must have access to adequate toilet and washing facilities, a place for warming up and eating their food and somewhere for storing clothing. However, these basic requirements are often neglected.

Both employers and the self-employed who have control over others doing construction work are responsible for providing or making available such welfare facilities as necessary. When they have overall control of the site, they are responsible for ensuring that legal duties are met by others who are working on the site. This may be done by one company or employer agreeing to provide the facilities for all those working at the site.

The welfare facilities should be sufficient for everybody who is working on the site and can be arranged separately or jointly with others. If facilities such as toilets and canteens provided by someone else are to be used, check that they are suitable and properly maintained. They should be kept clean, warm and properly ventilated. Before work starts on site make sure that what will be provided is adequate. Where the work is of short duration, arrangements still need to be made for welfare facilities. Portable facilities may be used or arrangements to use other existing facilities can be made (for example, when working at a factory, arrangements could be made to use the factory facilities), provided they are suitable.

Sanitary conveniences
The numbers of toilets required will depend on the number of people working on the site.

Wherever possible toilets should be flushed by water, but if this is not possible, use chemical toilets.

Rooms containing sanitary conveniences should be adequately ventilated and lit.

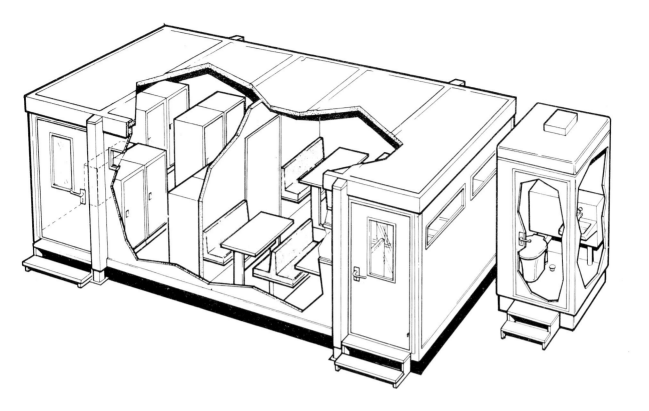

A wide range of portable welfare facilities like these are available. It may be possible when refurbishing buildings to use the facilities already on site.

Men and women may use the same toilet, provided it is in a separate room with a door which can be locked from the inside.

A washhand basin with water, soap and towels or dryers should be close to the toilets if the toilets are not near the other washing facilities provided on the site.

Washing facilities

On all sites, provide basins large enough to allow people to wash their faces, hands and forearms. All basins should have a supply of clean hot and cold, or warm, water. If mains water is not available, water supplied from a tank may be used. Soap and towels (either cloth or paper) or dryers should also be provided.

Where the work is particularly dirty or workers are exposed to toxic or corrosive substances (for example, during work in contaminated ground), showers may be needed.

Men and women can share basins used for washing their hands, faces and arms.

A shower may be used by both men and women provided that it is in a separate room with a lock on the inside of the door.

Rooms containing washing facilities should be sufficiently ventilated and lit.

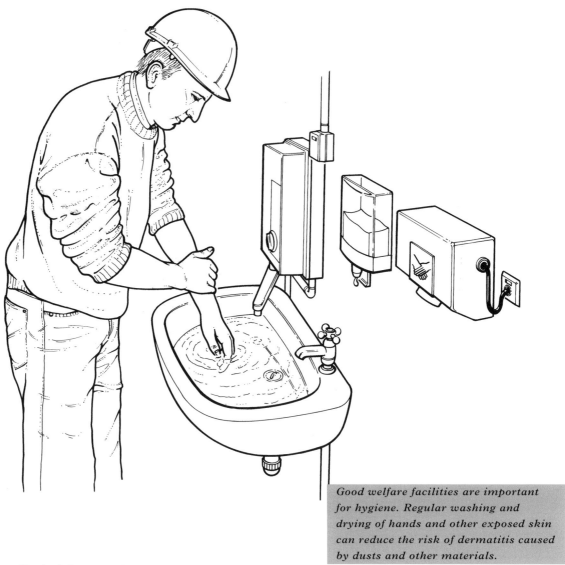

Good welfare facilities are important for hygiene. Regular washing and drying of hands and other exposed skin can reduce the risk of dermatitis caused by dusts and other materials.

Drinking water

Make sure there is a supply of drinking water. It is best if a tap direct from the mains is available. Otherwise bottles or tanks of water may be used for storage. If water is stored, it should be protected from possible contamination and changed often enough to prevent it from becoming stale or contaminated.

If it is possible to confuse the drinking water supply with other water supplies or other liquids which include:

•   those not fit for consumption (for example, water from storage tanks used for wheel washers); or

•   certain toxic materials (for example, from taps to pipelines in factories);

the tap should be clearly marked.

Cups or other drinking vessels should be available at the water tap, unless the water is supplied as an upward jet which can be drunk from easily (for example, a drinking fountain).

Storing and changing clothing

Make sure there are arrangements for storing:

- clothing not worn on site (for example, hats and overcoats);

- protective clothing needed for site work (for example, wellington boots, overalls etc).

Separate lockers might be needed, although on smaller sites the site office may be a suitable storage area, provided it is kept secure. Where there is a risk of protective site clothing contaminating everyday clothing, store items separately.

Where necessary for propriety, men and women should be able to change separately.

There should be somewhere to dry wet site clothing.

If electrical heaters are used, ensure that they are either fitted with a high temperature cut-out device or are properly ventilated. Many fires have been caused by placing too much clothing to dry on electrical heaters, making the appliance overheat.

Rest facilities

Facilities for taking breaks and meal breaks should be available. The facilities should provide shelter from the wind and rain and be heated as necessary.

The rest facilities should have:

- tables and chairs;

- a kettle or urn for boiling water;

- a means for preparing food (for example, a gas or electrical heating ring, or microwave oven).

It should be possible for non-smokers to use the facilities without suffering discomfort from tobacco smoke. It may be possible to prevent discomfort by increasing ventilation. If this cannot be done, it may be necessary to provide separate facilities for smokers and non-smokers, or prohibit smoking in the presence of non-smokers.

For small sites rest facilities can often be provided within the site office, or site hut, especially where this is one of the common portable units.

Remember: Open-flued gas heaters and gas cooking rings can produce carbon monoxide if not well ventilated. When poorly maintained, they also give rise to leaks of methane which can ignite or explode without warning. They should not be used in site huts, containers or other enclosed areas unless there is a permanent supply of fresh air, which cannot be closed off (a window which can be opened is not adequate as it is likely to be closed in cold weather).

Location of welfare facilities

Welfare facilities should be easily available to people working on the site. Toilets need to be easily accessible from where the work is being done. Washhand basins should be close to toilets. Washing facilities need to be near rest rooms so that people can wash before eating.

In most cases these facilities will be provided on site. Where work is done at an occupied premises, arrangements can be made with the occupier to use the facilities provided for the people who normally use the premises.

In some cases welfare and toilet facilities may be made available in nearby premises. This is acceptable, providing these arrangements are clear and agreed with the occupier of the premises. Such arrangements may be appropriate for short duration work or work done by mobile gangs.

If mobile gangs are being employed to work at a number of locations over a few days (for example, road repair and cable-laying gangs), facilities can be provided at a central location. This is on condition that they are available to workers within reasonable walking distance or within a reasonable time, taking into account any transport which is available. Workers should not be left to make their own arrangements on an 'as and when required' basis.

For more information, read HSE's information sheets on construction site welfare facilities.[4,5]

Emergency procedures

At most sites the most obvious emergency is fire. This is considered in greater detail on pages 14 to 16. However, there may be other problems, such as flooding in excavations, tunnels, work near the sea or rivers, waterworks etc or a risk from asphyxiation or toxic gases (see also Confined spaces, pages 59 to 61). Plan emergency procedures before work begins and put general precautions in place from the start of work. The general principles set out for dealing with fire risks can be applied to planning for other emergencies.

Some emergencies may require evacuation of the site, or part of the site, while others might involve the rescue of an injured person. For example, it may be necessary to plan how someone injured in a fall within a confined space or within a restricted plant room can be attended to by first aiders and the emergency services before being taken to a place of safety.

These signs should be white on green. The Health and Safety (Safety Signs and Signals) Regulations 1996 set standards for these signs. Existing signs which comply with BS 5499 differ in detail to those specified by the Regulations, but follow the same basic pattern and are still acceptable. See Safety signs and signals[6] for further details.

☐ When planning emergency procedures, routes and exits, take into account:

- the type of work being done on site (for example, extra precautions may be required to maintain routes down stairs during demolition);

- the characteristics and size of the site and the number and location of workplaces on the site (for example, a large site with people working at many locations will probably need bells or sirens at a number of places on the site to raise the alarm. On small sites with only two or three people working, a shouted warning may be adequate);

- the plant and equipment being used (for example, consider tower crane drivers, people working on suspended access equipment or where the exit may be blocked by equipment);

- the number of people likely to be present on the site at any one time (for example, on sites where many people work, escape routes need to be wide enough to allow everyone to get through doorways or down stairs easily without them becoming overcrowded); and

- the physical and chemical properties of substances or materials on or likely to be on the site (for example, work at petro-chemical installations or at sites where flammable paints or glues are in use may require an increased standard of ventilation).

☐ Take precautions to ensure:

- the likelihood of emergencies arising is as low as possible;

- everyone on site can be alerted in an emergency;

- everyone working on site (including contractors who may only be at the site for a few hours) knows what signal will be given if there is an emergency and knows what to do;

- someone who has been trained in what to do is on site while work is in progress and will take responsibility for co-ordinating procedures;

- emergency routes are available, kept clear, signed and adequately lit. Where necessary, (for example, when the site is not adequately lit by daylight for all periods when people are at work on the site) provide lighting which will come on automatically in an emergency (see page 17);

- there are arrangements for calling the emergency services. In particular let the Fire Brigade know about any work in tunnels, confined spaces or above 18 m (above this height specialist access equipment may be required) and anywhere else where specialised rescue equipment may be needed;

- there is adequate access to the site for the emergency services and that access does not become blocked by plant or material building up;

- arrangements for treating and recovering injured people are available;

- if an emergency does arise, someone is posted at the site entrance, or in another prominent position, so that they can direct the emergency services.

The rest of this section refers specifically to fire emergencies, but the basic principles can be applied to all site emergency planning.

Fire

Many solids, liquids and gases can catch fire and burn. It only takes a source of ignition, which may be a small flame or an electrical spark, together with air. Any outbreak of fire threatens the health and safety of those on site and will be costly in damage and delay. It can also be a hazard to people in surrounding properties. Fire can be a particular hazard in refurbishment work when there is a lot of dry timber and at the later stages of building jobs where a lot of flammable materials such as carpets and adhesives are in use.

Many fires can be avoided by careful planning and control of the work activities. Good housekeeping and site tidiness are important not only to prevent fire, but also to ensure that emergency routes do not become obstructed. Making site rules can help.

To prevent fires:

☐ use less easily ignited and fewer flammable materials, for example, use water-based or low solvent adhesives and paint;

☐ keep the quantity of flammables at the workplace to a minimum;

☐ always keep and carry flammable liquids in suitable closed containers;

☐ if work involving the use of highly flammable liquids or solids is being carried out, stop people smoking and don't allow other work activities involving potential ignition sources to take place nearby. For example, if floor coverings are being laid using solvent-based adhesives, don't allow soldering of pipes at the same time;

☐ ensure that pipes, barrels, tanks etc which may have contained flammable gases or liquids are purged or otherwise made safe before using hot cutting equipment, for example, a cutting torch or angle grinder. Any pipe or container may appear to be empty, but can contain enough material on its sides, or within rust or other sediments, to produce a flammable or explosive atmosphere within it when heated or disturbed. Advice from a specialist may be required;

☐ minimise the risk of gas leaks and fires involving gas fired plant:

• close valves on gas cylinders when not in use;

• regularly check hoses for wear and leaks;

• prevent oil or grease coming into contact with oxygen cylinder valves;

• do not leave bitumen boilers unattended when alight;

14

☐ store flammable solids, liquids and gases safely. Separate them from each other and from oxygen cylinders or oxidising materials. Keep them in ventilated secure stores or an outdoor storage area. Do not store them in or under occupied work areas or where they could obstruct or endanger escape routes;

☐ have an extinguisher to hand when doing hot work such as welding or using a disc cutter which produces sparks;

☐ check the site at lunch-time and at the end of the day to see that all plant and equipment that could cause a fire is turned off. Stop hot working an hour before people go home, as this will allow more time for smouldering fires to be identified; and

☐ provide closed metal containers to collect rubbish and remove them from the site regularly. Collect highly flammable waste such as solvent-soaked rags separately in closed fire-resisting containers.

Precautions in case of fire

If a fire should break out, people must be able to escape from it. To achieve this consider:

☐ **means of giving warning:** Set up a system to alert people on site; this could be a self-contained fire alarm unit, klaxon, whistle or even word-of-mouth on a small site. Any warning needs to be distinctive, audible above other noise and recognisable by everyone;

☐ **means of escape:** Plan escape routes and ensure they remain available and unobstructed. For work areas above or below ground, provide well separated alternative ways to ground level where possible. Protect routes by installing the permanent fire separation and fire doors as soon as possible. It is important that escape routes give access to a safe place where people can assemble and be accounted for. In a large chemical plant this may be a safety refuge, while on a small site the pavement outside may be adequate. Signs might be needed if people are not familiar with the escape routes. Make sure that adequate lighting is provided for enclosed escape routes - emergency lighting may be required (see page 17);

☐ **means of fighting fire:** As well as providing fire extinguishers for hot work, fire extinguishers should be located at identified fire points around the site. The extinguishers should be appropriate to the nature of the potential fire:

• wood, paper and cloth - water extinguisher;

• flammable liquids - dry powder or foam extinguisher;

• electrical - carbon dioxide (CO_2) extinguisher.

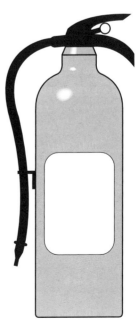

People should be trained in how to use extinguishers.

If the building being worked in is occupied, for example, an office, hotel or hospital, make sure the work does not interfere with the escape route from the building, or any fire separation, alarms, dry risers, or sprinkler systems. Check this with the occupier of the building or the Fire Brigade.

Fire doors should never be locked, left open or removed. Keep existing wet and dry risers ready for use and install any new ones as soon as possible.

For more information, read *Fire safety in construction work,*[7] *Fire prevention on construction sites*[8] and *Construction sites fire prevention checklist.*[9]

Site tidiness

Plan how the site will be kept tidy. In particular, walkways and stairs should be kept free of tripping hazards such as trailing wires and loose materials. This is especially important for emergency routes. Remove nails from loose timbers to prevent foot and other injuries. Clear paper, timber offcuts and other flammable materials to reduce fire risks.

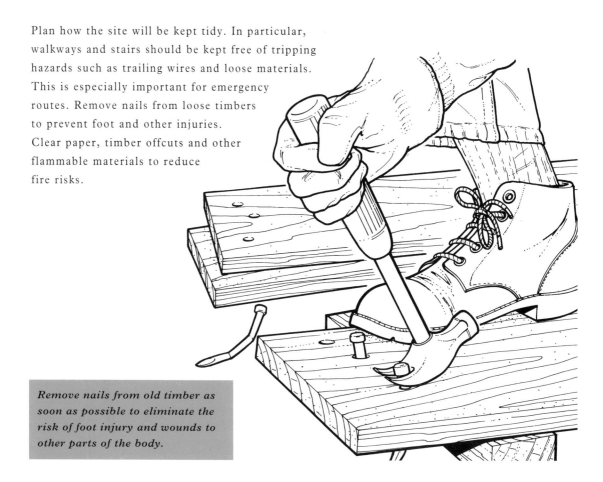

Remove nails from old timber as soon as possible to eliminate the risk of foot injury and wounds to other parts of the body.

Lighting

Every part of the site which is in use should, as far as possible, be arranged so that natural light is available for people to see to do their work and move about the site safely. Where natural light is inadequate or not available, artificial lighting should be provided.

Where work will continue outside daylight hours or the building or structure is enclosed, artificial lighting will be required. Make sure that any artificial lighting does not change the apparent colour or visibility of any safety signs or other safety-related items such as fire extinguishers.

With both daylight and artificial light, shadows can obscure hazards both at the workplace (for example, making it difficult to see the blade of a cutting disc or the bit of a drill) and on the site generally (for example, at stair-wells). If necessary, provide extra lighting to illuminate shadow areas.

Where failure of the primary artificial lighting would be a risk to the health or safety of anyone (for example, someone working on a tower scaffold in a basement may fall while trying to descend in the dark), provide emergency lighting. Where it is not possible to have lighting which comes on automatically when the primary lighting fails, torches or other similar lights may provide suitable lighting.

In addition, emergency routes (the corridors, passageways etc which people must follow in an emergency to escape from danger), should be kept well lit while there are workers on the site. Where daylight provides adequate lighting, no further action is required. Where emergency routes need artificial light, also provide emergency lighting which comes on if the primary lighting fails (for example, battery or emergency generator powered lighting). See also emergency procedures, pages 12 to 14. Emergency lighting does not have to provide the same level of lighting as under normal circumstances; merely enough to enable escape.

For further information, read *Lighting at work*.[10]

Doors and gates

As part of providing safe access and egress, it may be necessary to provide doors and gates. These can range from the existing doors within a house under refurbishment to the installation of a new door or gate as part of a new building.

It may be necessary to fit devices to doors and gates which allow them to be used properly. Doors which open onto traffic routes may need vision panels or windows. Sliding doors and gates may need stop ends to prevent them coming off their runners or tracks. Rising doors or gates may need a means of preventing them from falling back.

Storage areas

Set up storage areas for plant, materials, flammable substances (for example, foam plastics, flammable liquids and gases such as propane) and hazardous substances (for example, pesticides and timber treatment chemicals). Flammable materials will usually need to be stored away from other materials and protected from accidental ignition. Do not store materials where they obstruct access routes or where they could interfere with emergency escape. For example, do not store flammable materials next to fire exits.

If materials are stored at height (for example, on top of a container or on a scaffold gantry), make sure necessary guard rails are in place if people could fall when stacking or collecting materials or equipment.

Site rules

Clients may insist on certain safety precautions, especially where their business continues at the premises while construction work is in progress. It may assist everyone if site rules are applied. Site rules might cover, for example, safety helmets, safety footwear, site transport, fire prevention, site tidiness, hearing protection or permit-to-work systems. Make sure everybody knows and follows any rules relevant to them.

First aid

First aid can save lives, reduce pain and help an injured person make a quicker recovery. The Health and Safety (First Aid) Regulations 1981 set out the basic requirements. The number of qualified first aiders needed depends on the risk of injury and ill health on site. There should always be on site:

- a first aid box with enough equipment to cope with the number of workers on site;

- an appointed person who knows how to contact the accident and emergency services;

- information telling workers the name of the appointed person or first aider and where to find them. A notice in the site hut is a good way of doing this.

The first-aid arrangements should cover shift working, night and weekend working where this is carried out.

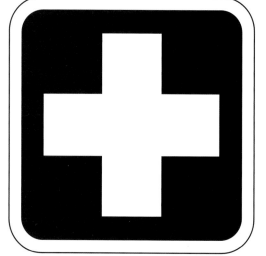

HSE's leaflet *Basic advice on first aid at work*[11] gives more advice.

CONTROL AND SUPERVISION

Section 2 of this book identifies a range of hazards common on most sites. It also tells how a hazard (something with potential to cause harm) can be identified, so that the risk it results in (the likelihood and severity of that harm) can be controlled. Before work starts:

☐   consider if there are any hazards you can avoid altogether;

☐   decide which hazards need to be controlled;

☐   consider the best ways of controlling them; and then

☐   having decided what needs to be done, make sure it happens.

Check that:

☐   everyone is properly trained and competent;

☐   they have the equipment they need; and

☐   agreed work methods are put into practice.

Good site supervision is essential to maintaining healthy and safe conditions. It should be made clear to supervisors exactly what it is they are expected to do and how they are expected to do it. The greater the risk, the greater the degree of control and supervision required.

Consult people working at the site and their representaives- their views about health and safety should be considered. For further information, see *A guide to the Health and Safety (Consultation with Employees) Regulations 1996.*[12]

When people, either employees, other contractors or visitors first come to site, it is important that they receive information about the site hazards and the steps that have been taken to control the risks. Make sure that the person running the site can be easily identified; if there is a site office, sign it clearly. A site plan showing the office location placed at the site entrance, together with an instruction that all visitors report to the site office, can be helpful. The principal contractor has a duty to take reasonable steps to ensure that only authorised people are allowed where construction work is being done.

People who are going to work on the site for the first time should be briefed about risks, welfare facilities and site rules. One way of doing this is by making sure the site supervisor speaks to them before they start work. They might also be given an information sheet or relevant information might be displayed on a notice board prominently placed near the site entrance. Remember, many people are killed and seriously injured during the first few days that they work at a site.

Health and safety checks can be incorporated into normal progress and quality checks carried out by supervisors and managers. Specific additional checks on higher risk work may also be needed.

Carrying out routine checks from time to time reminds everyone that health and safety matters!

NOTIFYING THE SITE TO HSE

If the construction work is expected to either:

*   last longer than 30 days; or

*   involve more than 500 person days of construction work;

HSE should be notified in writing before construction work starts. The notification should be sent to the HSE office nearest to the proposed site (details on pages 116 to 117).

A form (Form 10 rev) can be used for notification. A copy of the form can be found at the back of this book, and may be photocopied and used for notification. Forms are also available from HSE offices. It is not essential that this form is used for notification, but the information required on Form 10 must be provided in writing to HSE. A copy of the notification details should be displayed at a place on site where it can be easily read.

Where CDM applies, notification of the project will be the responsibility of the planning supervisor (see page 107). The planning supervisor should update the information as it becomes available (for example, when the principal contractor is appointed). If CDM does not apply, it will be the responsibility of the contractors to notify the site to HSE. If someone has already sent a notification, a second notification is not required. Ask whoever is co-ordinating the work if notification has been sent.

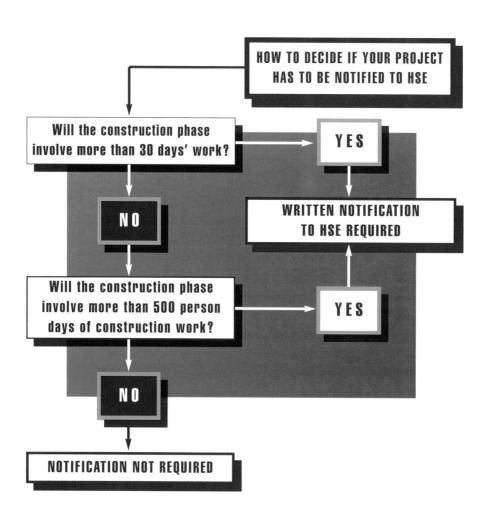

MONITORING AND REVIEWING

Checking health and safety precautions are being taken is as important as checking progress and quality. Site supervisors need to see that the firm considers the fulfilment of their health and safety responsibilities as an essential part of their job. Section 3 gives more information about this subject.

Part of monitoring is to carry out inspections of plant and materials. The specific requirements for inspection of scaffolds and excavations is set out below.

PLACE OF WORK REQUIRING INSPECTIONS

Working platforms etc

Where it is possible for a person to fall 2 m or more from a working platform, the platform and associated parts need to be inspected by a competent person:

☐ before first use;

☐ after substantial alteration;

☐ after any event likely to have affected its stability, for example, following strong winds; and

☐ at regular intervals not exceeding seven days.

The person in control must have the inspections carried out by a competent person. Whoever controls the activities of others who use a scaffold also needs to ensure it is safe before they use it for the first time.

If the competent person is not satisfied that work can be carried out safely, they should advise the person for whom the inspection was carried out as soon as possible. The workplace should not be used until the defects have been put right.

A written report should be made following most inspections (see page 22).

Excavations

Excavations which need to be supported or battered back to prevent danger must be inspected. The person in control of the excavation must arrange for a competent person to carry out these inspections:

☐ at the start of the shift before work begins;

☐ after any event likely to have affected its stability; and

☐ after any accidental fall of rock, earth or other material.

If the competent person is not satisfied that work can be carried out safely, they should advise the person for whom the inspection was carried out as soon as possible. The workplace should not be used until the defects have been put right.

Remember the passage of construction plant close to an excavation will put additional loading on the excavation. Any supports must be able to carry such loadings.

Cofferdams and caissons also need to be inspected.

A written report should be made following most inspections.

Reports

The competent person needs to complete a report of the inspections before the end of the working period and provide the report or a copy to the person on whose behalf the inspection was carried out within 24 hours, except that:

- an inspection is required whenever a working platform, associated part or any personal suspension equipment is:

  - taken into use for the first time; or

  - substantially altered.

  However, when more than one such inspection is carried out within any 24-hour period, only one report of inspection needs to be completed;

- no report is required following the inspection of a mobile tower scaffold, unless it remains erected in the same place for more than seven days;

- for an excavation, only one written report is required within any seven day period, unless there has been a collapse/fall of material or other event likely to affect stability. In this case an inspection and report are required before work starts again.

The report should contain the following information:

☐ name and address of person on whose behalf the inspection was carried out;

☐ location of the workplace inspected;

☐ description of workplace or part of workplace inspected (including any plant, equipment and materials, if any);

☐ date and time of inspection;

☐ details of any matter identified that could lead to a risk to the health or safety of anyone;

☐ details of any action taken as a result of any matter identified in the last point;

☐   details of any more action considered necessary; and

☐   the name and position of the person making the report.

At the back of this book is a suggested format which may be reproduced or copied for recording this information. The suggested form does not have to be used - any form containing the required information can be used. The reverse of the form summarises the requirements for timing and frequency of inspections.

The report, or a copy, should be given to the person in control of the workplace.
They should keep it on site until work is complete and then retain it at their office for a further three months.

Also included at the back of the book is a health and safety checklist. This list covers issues which need to be addressed on almost every site. The list can be used by those planning work to help them decide if they have addressed the most significant risks before work starts. It can also be used as a tool for site supervisors and others who may need to monitor site conditions. The checklist is a guide; there may be additional matters at some sites which are vital to address. Also items may be included in the list which are irrelevant at other sites. The checklist may be photocopied.

REPORTING ACCIDENTS AND WORK-RELATED DISEASES

Employers must report to HSE any accidents which happen to their employees. Whoever is in control of the site must also report those accidents which involve a self-employed worker or member of the public. Details of requirements for accident reporting are given on page 108 (RIDDOR '95). Investigating accidents and near misses can help identify circumstances where more precautions are required or where procedures are not being followed.

2: CONSTRUCTION WORK: THE ESSENTIALS OF HEALTH AND SAFETY

INTRODUCTION

In construction work many of the hazards are obvious. Most of them can be found on almost every site. The causes of accidents are well known and often repeated. Too often hazards are just seen as an inevitable part of the job, so no action is taken to control the risks they create. Consequently, the rate of accidents and ill health remains high. Action is needed to change this.

This section identifies the most common causes of death, injury and ill health and sets out straightforward precautions. Applying this advice will make work safer and, in most cases, improve efficiency. Some activities (eg roof work and steel erection) are considered in detail, but in general most operations will present a number of hazards which are dealt with on a number of pages.

Examples

Painting may include:
*   a risk of falls (see pages 26 to 42);

*   paints and solvents which may be health hazards (see hazardous substances, pages 73 to 76, and choosing personal protective equipment, page 82).

Fitting out in an office being refurbished may involve:
*   a risk of falls (see pages 26 to 42);

*   electrical risks from portable equipment (see pages 84 to 87); and

*   a risk of exposure to asbestos (see pages 77 to 79).

The information in this section will help those carrying out risk assessments (see pages 94 to 95) by explaining how to identify hazards and select control measures. In finalising an appropriate safe system of work for any construction job, it will be necessary to consider the particular nature of the site and the detail of the operations to be carried out. Where the Construction (Design and Management) Regulations 1994 (CDM) apply (see pages 101 to 103), the health and safety plan may provide additional useful information.

SAFE PLACE OF WORK

Any place where work is carried out should be safe and free of risks to health at all times. This includes access to and egress from the workplace. Sufficient space to work safely should be provided.

Can the hazards be avoided?

This is the first question. For example, the need to paint at height can be reduced if materials are brought to site ready-finished.

If not, can the risks be controlled?

In many cases it will not be possible to avoid the hazard altogether, so the risks need to be controlled by making sure the work can be done from a safe place. Consider the size and position of the place where work is to be carried out. People need adequate space to do their work, and space for the plant and equipment that will be used for the tasks.

When planning for a safe workplace, also consider access by people other than those doing the work. Where it is possible that members of the public or other contractors may be at risk (for example, from falling materials), take precautions to exclude or protect them.

WORKING AT HEIGHT

Falls are the largest cause of accidental death in the construction industry. They account for 50% of all fatalities. Most accidents involving falls could have been prevented if the right equipment had been provided and properly used. All falls need to be prevented. However, specific precautions need to be taken (guard rails, barriers, etc - see pages 27 to 28) where it is possible to fall two metres (2 m) or more. Even if the fall is less than 2 m, it may be necessary to protect the worker, for example if they are working above starter-bars - assess the risk.

When planning for work at height, consider where the work will be done. Obviously the first choice will be any existing structure which allows safe access and provides a safe working place. Where it is not possible to work safely from the existing structure, an extra working platform will be needed.

Rules to prevent falls

☐ Don't work at height unless it is essential.

☐ Make sure the working platform is secure. Check that it:

- will support the weight of workers using it and any materials and equipment they are likely to use or store on it;

- is stable and will not overturn. For example, scaffolds usually need to be tied to a supporting structure. Mobile elevating work platforms (MEWPs) may not be safe on uneven or sloping ground;

- provides adequate working space; and

- is footed on stable ground or on a stable support or structure.

☐ Provide guard rails, barriers etc at open edges, including edges of floors, floor openings, edges of roofs and edges of working platforms.

The nature or duration of the work may also influence what working platform is most appropriate. Traditionally much work has been done from scaffolding. However, other means of access such as MEWPs, tower scaffolds, personal suspension equipment (such as rope access techniques and boatswain's chairs) and ladders, offer advantages and disadvantages. It is essential to consider what risks there may be in erecting the access equipment as well as using it.

☐ Matters which need to be considered when selectng a type of work platform or means of access to the workplace include:

- space available on the site. Each type of platform requires minimum amounts of space, for example, MEWPS need outriggers - can you fit them in?;

- the type of work to be carried out, eg will it require heavy loads on the platform?;

- how long the work will last;

- what risks there will be during erection of the platform;

- how difficult the platform will be to maintain;

- how many people will need to use the equipment;

- can the equipment be stabilised, eg can the scaffold be tied?; and

- whether part of the structure can be provided early in the work so that there is a permanent working platform.

Guard rails and toe boards

Suitable precautions should be taken to prevent falls. Guard rails, toe boards and other similar barriers should be provided whenever someone could fall 2 m or more.

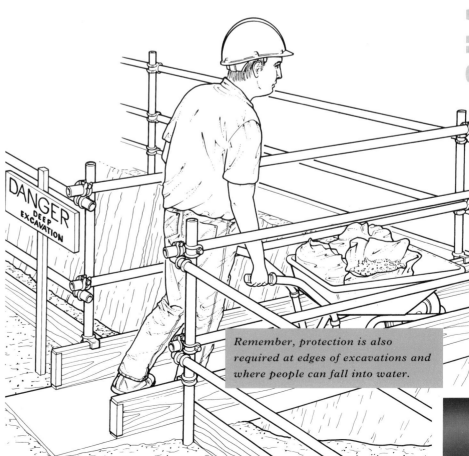

Remember, protection is also required at edges of excavations and where people can fall into water.

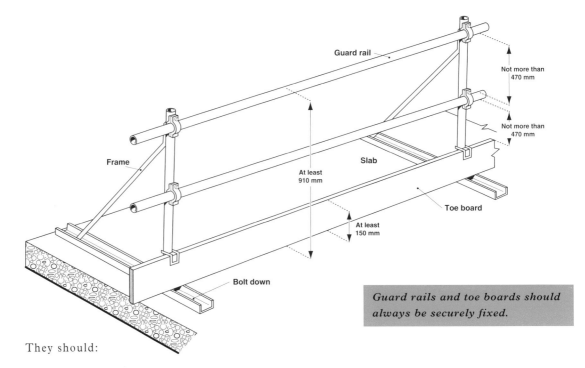

Guard rail

Not more than 470 mm

Not more than 470 mm

Frame

Slab

At least 910 mm

Toe board

At least 150 mm

Bolt down

Guard rails and toe boards should always be securely fixed.

They should:

☐ be strong and rigid enough to prevent people from falling and be able to withstand other loads likely to be placed on them. For example, guard rails fitted with brick guards need to be capable of supporting the weight of stacks of bricks which could fall against them;

☐ be fixed to a structure, or part of a structure capable of supporting them;

☐ include:

• a main guard rail at least 910 mm above any edge from which people are liable to fall;

• a toe board at least 150 mm high;

• a sufficient number of intermediate guard rails or suitable alternatives positioned so that the unprotected gap does not exceed 470 mm. Where the barrier is solid, or the space between the upper part of the barrier and the toe board is completely occupied by mesh (for example, a brick guard) or similar, an intermediate guard rail is not required.

Barriers other than guard rails and toe boards can be used, so long as they are at least 910 mm high, secure and provide an equivalent standard of protection against falls and materials rolling, or being kicked, from any edges.

If the risk comes from falling through openings or fragile material (for example, rooflights or asbestos roof sheets), an alternative to guard rails or a barrier is to cover the opening or material. Any covering should be:

☐ strong enough to support any loads likely to be placed on it (including the weight of a person); and

☐ fixed in position to prevent accidental dislodgement. To prevent people removing coverings, mark them with a warning (for example, 'Hole below - do not remove').

If possible, discourage passage across covers by directing people around them, for example, using a high-visibility tape barrier.

Summary of steps to take before working at height

☐ Check there is a safe method of getting to and from the work area.

☐ Decide what particular equipment will be suitable for the job and the conditions on site.

☐ Make sure work platforms and any edges from which people are likely to fall have guard rails and toe boards or other barriers.

☐ Make sure that the equipment needed is delivered to site in good time and that the site has been prepared for it.

☐ Check that the equipment is in good condition and make sure that whoever puts the equipment together is trained and knows what they are doing.

☐ Make sure those who use the equipment are supervised so that they use it properly. The more specialised the equipment (for example, boatswain's chairs and rope access equipment), the greater the degree of training and supervision required to ensure safety.

☐ Check any equipment provided by another company is safe on site before using it.

☐ Find out who to tell if any defects need to be remedied or modifications need to be made and keep them informed.

When selecting a means of access, remember:

☐ only when it is not practicable to provide a work platform with guard rails should other means of access (for example, boatswain's chairs or rope access techniques) be used;

☐ only when no other method is practicable, or risk assessment shows other methods are safer when work platforms cannot comply with all requirements for safe work (eg a guard rail has to be removed to land materials), should a way of arresting falls (for example, a harness and lines or nets) be relied upon;

☐ if no other means of providing a safe place of work at height is available, then appropriately anchored harness should be worn. However, whenever harnesses are used a method must be available to enable people to be rescued should they fall and be left suspended in their harness;

☐ nets may also be needed to protect those working to put guard rails or other protection in place;

☐ ladders should always be secured if possible. They should be primarily used for access and only be used as workplaces to do light work of short duration, and then only if it is safe to do so. It is generally safer to use a tower scaffold (see pages 32-33) or MEWP (see page 35) even for short-term work. Heavy work activity such as drilling or carrying heavy loads should never be carried out from a ladder. When using a ladder ensure that the person on the ladder always has three points of contact, ie two legs and a hand. People should never have to lean sideways when up a ladder.

□ when selecting a safe system of work at heights, all the risks have to be considered before one method is selected. For example, if nets are selected, is there adequate clearance under the nets to prevent injury to those who may fall into them? If harnesses are used, is there sufficient clearance from the ground to allow the shock absorbing lanyard or inertia reel to fully extend?

□ before any work at height, check that there is adequate clearance for equipment. For example, overhead power lines can be a risk when erecting scaffolds or using MEWPs; there can be a risk of crushing against nearby structures when mobile access platforms are manoeuvred.

Safe working platforms

Working platforms are the parts of structures, MEWPs, cradles etc upon which people stand while working. As well as being adequately supported and provided with guard rails or barriers, working platforms should be:

□ wide enough to allow people to pass back and forth safely and to use any equipment or material necessary for their work at that place and in any case, at least 600 mm wide;

□ free of openings and traps through which people's feet could pass, causing them to trip, fall or be injured in any other way;

□ constructed to prevent materials from falling. As well as toe boards or similar protection at the edge of the platform, the platform itself should be constructed to prevent any object which may be used on the platform from falling through gaps or holes, causing injury to people working below. For scaffolds, a close-boarded platform would suffice, although for work over public areas, a double-boarded platform sandwiching a polythene sheet may be needed. If MEWPs or cradles are used and they have meshed platform floors, the mesh should be fine enough to prevent materials, especially nails and bolts, from slipping through; and

□ kept free of tripping and slipping hazards. Where necessary, provide handholds and footholds. Keep platforms clean and tidy. Do not allow mud to build up on platforms.

General access scaffolds

For any scaffold make sure:

□ it is designed, erected, altered and dismantled by competent people and the work is directed by a competent supervisor. Scaffolders should always adopt methods of work to prevent falls during the erection of scaffolding. This will normally mean wearing harnesses. For further information on erecting scaffolding see NASC guidance note *The use of fall arrest equipment whilst erecting, altering and dismantling scaffolding;*[13]

□ it should never be erected over people or busy pavements. If the work presents a danger to the public, it should be done during quiet times, eg early morning, or the pavement should be closed with a diversion provided or a crash deck erected over the pavement.

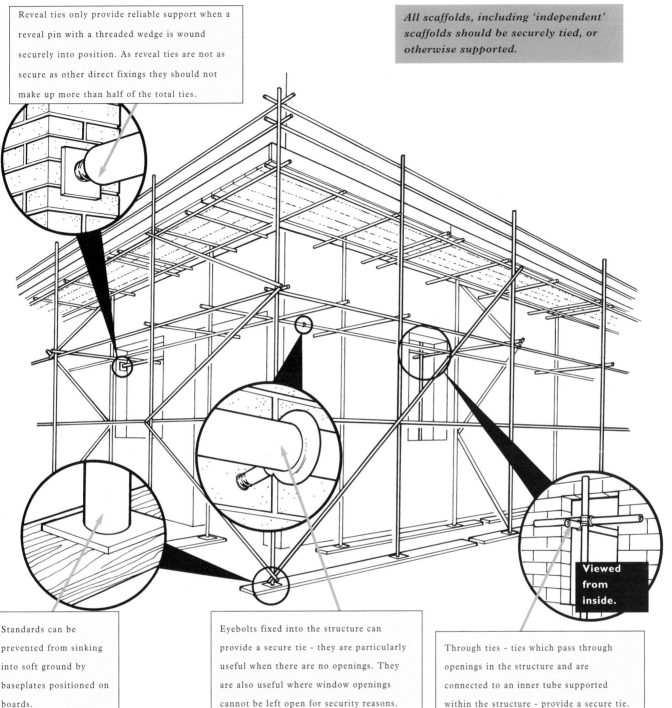

Reveal ties only provide reliable support when a reveal pin with a threaded wedge is wound securely into position. As reveal ties are not as secure as other direct fixings they should not make up more than half of the total ties.

All scaffolds, including 'independent' scaffolds should be securely tied, or otherwise supported.

Standards can be prevented from sinking into soft ground by baseplates positioned on boards.

Eyebolts fixed into the structure can provide a secure tie - they are particularly useful when there are no openings. They are also useful where window openings cannot be left open for security reasons.

Through ties - ties which pass through openings in the structure and are connected to an inner tube supported within the structure - provide a secure tie.

Viewed from inside.

☐ it is based on a firm, level foundation. The ground or foundation should be capable of supporting the weight of the scaffold and any loads likely to be placed on it. Watch out for voids such as basements or drains, or patches of soft ground, which could collapse when loaded. Provide extra support as necessary;

☐ it is braced and tied into a permanent structure or otherwise stabilised. Rakers only provide stability when they are braced and footed adequately; single-tube rakers alone do not usually provide this and need to be braced to prevent buckling. Put ties in place as the scaffold is erected and only remove them in stages as it is struck. If a tie is removed to allow work to proceed, an equivalent tie should be provided nearby to maintain stability. Proprietary system scaffolds should be erected and tied according to the manufacturers' instructions;

☐ it is capable of supporting loads likely to be placed on it. Scaffolds are not usually designed to support heavy loads on their working platforms. If intending to load out platforms, tell whoever is providing the scaffold - a special design might be required. Most work at height falls into three categories: light duty, medium duty and heavy duty: obtain the class of scaffold appropriate to the work you are doing;

☐ you never sheet a scaffold without informing the supplier you are going to do so;

☐ platforms are fully boarded and wide enough for the work and for access;

☐ scaffold boards are properly supported and not overhanging excessively (for example, no more than four times the thickness of the board);

☐ there is safe ladder or other access onto the work platforms; and

☐ it is suitable for the task before it is used and checked whenever it is substantially altered or adversely affected by, for example, high winds.

Before using any scaffold, make sure that it is safe and suitable for the intended job. See inspections and reports on pages 21 to 23.

Tower scaffolds

Tower scaffolds can be erected quickly and can give good safe access. However, they are involved in numerous accidents each year. These accidents usually happen because the tower has either not been erected properly or has not been used properly.

If a tower scaffold is going to be used:

☐ follow the manufacturer's instructions for erection, use and dismantling. Have a copy of the instruction manual available - if the scaffold has been hired, the hirer ought to provide this information;

☐ the tower must be vertical and the legs should rest properly on firm, level ground;

☐ lock any wheels and outriggers - base plates provide greater stability if the tower does not have to be moved;

☐ provide a safe way to get to and from the work platform, for example, internal ladders. Climbing up the outside of the tower may pull it over;

☐ provide edge protection (guard rails and toe boards);

☐ provide guard rails and toe boards on any intermediate platforms which are also being used as working platforms or for storing materials;

☐ tie the tower rigidly to the structure it is serving or provide other additional support if:

· the tower is sheeted;

· it is likely to be exposed to strong winds;

- it is used for carrying out grit blasting or water jetting;

- heavy materials are lifted up the outside of the tower; or

- the tower base is too small to ensure stability for the height of the platform.

If ties are needed, check that they are put in place as required when the scaffold is erected. Make sure they are checked from time to time (for details of inspection requirements, see page 21 and the reverse of the inspection form at the back of the book) and that necessary ties are kept in place when the scaffold is dismantled.

Do not:

- use a ladder footed on the working platform or apply other horizontal loads which could tilt the tower;

- overload the working platform;

- fix ties to the centres of thin walled aluminium tubes.

- move the tower by applying the necessary force at the platform level; or

- climb up the outside of the tower to reach the platform.

When moving a mobile tower:

☐   check that there are no power lines or overhead obstructions in the way;

☐   check that there are no holes or dips in the ground;

☐   do not allow people or materials to remain on it as towers tip over very easily when being moved.

For further information on tower scaffolds, read *Tower scaffolds.*[14]

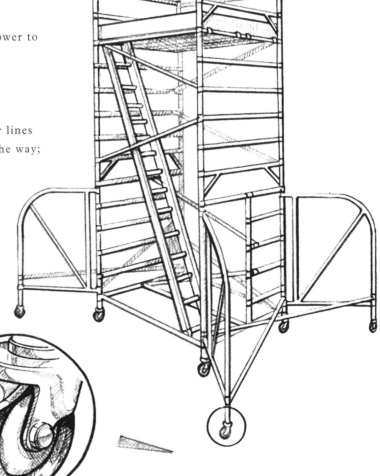

Always lock the castors of mobile towers after moving them.

Mobile and suspended access equipment

Where it is not possible to work from the existing structure and the use of a scaffold working platform is not appropriate, a range of mobile access equipment including mobile elevating work platforms (MEWPs), suspended cradles, mast climbing work platforms (MCWPs), boatswain's chairs or seats, and rope access equipment can be used.

Those using this type of equipment should be trained and competent to operate it. They should learn emergency and evacuation procedures so that they know what to do, for example, if the power to the platform fails, or fire breaks out in the building being worked on. With many pieces of equipment, more than one person will be needed to ensure safe operation.

Before work starts, check that:

☐ a handover certificate is provided by the installer. The certificate should cover how to deal with emergencies, operate, check and maintain the equipment, and state its safe working load;

☐ equipment is installed, modified and dismantled only by competent specialists;

☐ there is a current report of thorough examination for the equipment;

☐ areas of the site where people may be struck by the platform or falling materials have been barriered off or similar. Debris fans or covered walkways may also be required;

☐ systems are in place to prevent people within the building being struck by the platform as it rises or descends and prevent the platform coming into contact with open windows or similar obstructions which could cause it to tip;

☐ supports are protected from damage (for example, by being struck by passing vehicles or by interference from vandals);

☐ the equipment can be protected from adverse weather. High winds can tilt platforms and make them unstable. Establish a maximum safe wind speed for operation. Storms and snow falls can also damage platforms, so they should be inspected before use after severe weather.

At the end of each day check that:

☐ the platform is cleared of tools and equipment;

☐ all power has been switched off and, where appropriate, power cables have been secured and made dead;

☐ the equipment is secured where it will not be accessible to vandals or trespassers;

☐ notices are attached to the equipment warning that it is out of service and must not be used; and

☐ check the shift report for warnings of malfunction etc.

Mobile elevating work platforms (MEWPs)

Mobile elevating work platforms (MEWPs) can provide excellent safe access to high level work. When using a MEWP make sure that:

☐   whoever is operating it is fully trained and competent;

☐   the work platform is provided with guard rails and toe boards or other suitable barriers;

☐   it is used on firm and level ground. The ground may have to be prepared in advance;

☐   its tyres are properly inflated;

☐   any outriggers are extended and chocked as necessary before raising the platform; and

☐   everyone knows what to do if the machine fails with the platform in the raised position.

Do not:

•   operate MEWPs close to overhead cables or other dangerous machinery;

•   allow a knuckle, or elbow, of the arm to protrude into a traffic route when working near vehicles;

•   move the equipment with the platform in the raised position unless the equipment is designed to allow this to be done safely (check the manufacturer's instructions).

Some MEWPs are described as suitable for 'rough terrain'. This usually means that they are safe to use on some uneven or undulating ground - but check their limitations in the manufacturer's handbook before taking them onto unprepared or sloping ground.

Wearing a harness with a fall restraint lanyard (see page 39) attached to the platform can provide extra protection against falls, especially while the platform is in motion.

See also general advice about mobile and suspended access equipment (page 34).

A wide range of MEWPs is available to provide access for almost any work at height.

Mast climbing work platforms

This equipment is often used when carrying out repairs to or refurbishment of high rise buildings. MCWPs are designed to provide access to working positions - they are not designed to act as material hoists.

Only specialists should erect, alter or dismantle mast platforms. It is particularly important that the correct sequence is followed. Serious accidents have occurred when ties have been removed or outriggers have not been properly extended during alterations.

A great advantage of using mast platforms is that those using them can be protected from adverse weather as many types can be provided with screens and a roof to the platform. Enclosures to platforms can increase wind loads. The supplier must always be consulted before fixing them.

When mast platforms are used, make sure:

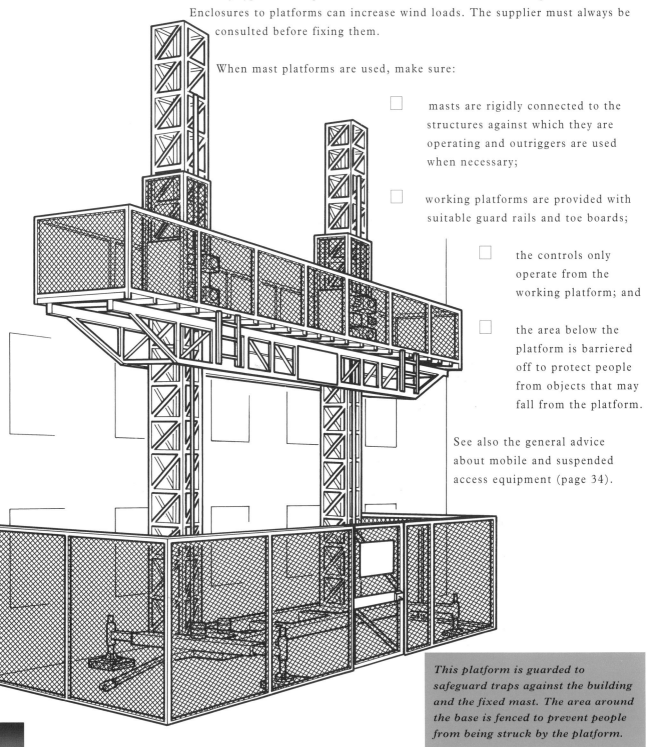

☐ masts are rigidly connected to the structures against which they are operating and outriggers are used when necessary;

☐ working platforms are provided with suitable guard rails and toe boards;

☐ the controls only operate from the working platform; and

☐ the area below the platform is barriered off to protect people from objects that may fall from the platform.

See also the general advice about mobile and suspended access equipment (page 34).

This platform is guarded to safeguard traps against the building and the fixed mast. The area around the base is fenced to prevent people from being struck by the platform.

Temporarily suspended access cradles and platforms

Accidents happen during installation, use and dismantling of temporary cradles. Most accidents happen because of:

- unsafe access to and from the cradle;

- insufficient or poorly secured counterweights and holding down systems;

- failure of the cradle platform or components such as drop nose pins and bolts;

- failure of winches, climbing devices, safety gear and ropes usually as a result of poor maintenance; and

- failure to follow the manufacturer's instructions on erection and dismantling.

Equipment should be selected, installed, thoroughly examined and tested to ensure that it is suitable for its intended purpose. Cradles should only be used by suitably trained and competent workers.

When using cradles check that:

☐ the cradle has adequate guard rails and toe boards and material cannot fall from or through the cradle's base;

☐ the equipment is capable of fitting closely to the building and where buffers or rollers are fitted, they will run against suitable features on the building;

☐ the building is capable of carrying the loads placed upon it, particularly under the counterweights and under the fulcrum (or pivot point) of the outrigger. The advice of a structural engineer may be needed;

☐ jib spacing matches the cradle length and, when the cradle can move, adequate stops are provided to prevent the cradle running off the end of the track;

☐ jib length and counterweights are specified to give a factor of safety against overturning of no less than three;

☐ a secondary safety rope fitted with a fall arrest device is provided and used;

☐ adequate operating instructions and technical support is available. If the equipment is hired, the supplier should be able to advise;

☐ the cradle is not overloaded and loads are placed on the platform as uniformly as possible;

☐ there is safe access into the cradle. Access at ground level is safest. If access is from the roof, the cradle should be secured to prevent it swinging away from the building. Access must be possible without the need to climb up or down the suspension ropes. Also, if access is from the roof, or other raised platform, suitable means to prevent falls from roof edges will be required (for example, guard rails and toe boards); and

☐ there is a plan for rescuing the operator if the crane fails while at a high level.

Even where these precautions have been taken, accidents are still possible. For example, if a motor of a powered cradle fails, it can make the cradle tip or people may overbalance and fall while reaching out of the cradle. Safety harnesses can save lives in these circumstances. Harnesses should be attached to suitable anchorage points within the cradle or platform (such as the motor mounting points) or attached to running lines rigged in the cradle. The harness lanyards should be kept as short as possible, while allowing operators to reach their place of work. For further advice on the use of harnesses, see page 39.

It is important that a thorough visual pre-use check for obvious faults is carried out before each use. In addition, a weekly inspection should be carried out by a competent person and a record made of that inspection. See also the general advice about mobile and suspended access equipment (page 34). Before taking a temporary scaffold access platform into use, the following should be checked daily:

☐ The platform should be structurally sound: lift it off the ground, say 1 m, and inspect for excessive deflections;

☐ While it is off the ground, carry out a tactile inspection of critical connectors;

☐ Make sure that it runs freely up and down - try it out; and

☐ Check that lines of communication work properly.

At the end of the day/shift, the following at least should be done:

☐ the platform cleared of tools and equipment;

☐ all power switched off and, where appropriate, power cables secured and made dead;

☐ the equipment secured where it will not be accessible to vandals or trespassers;

☐ notices attached to the equipment, warning that it is out of service and must not be used; and

☐ shift report checked for warnings of malfunction etc.

Boatswain's chairs/seats

Boatswain's chairs and seats can be used for light, short-term work. They should only be used where it is not practicable to provide a working platform. In general, use a chair which consists of a seat with a back, a central suspension point and a carrying point for tools.

Whether a chair or seat is used, the user should be attached to the suspension system by a harness and lanyard to protect against falls (see page 39). See also the general advice about mobile and suspended access equipment (page 34).

The worker using this boatswain's chair is protected by a harness. The tool and equipment bucket is rigidly fixed to and supported by the chair.

Rope access techniques

This technique can be used for inspection and some short-term light-duration construction work. It should only be used where access from a working platform is not practicable. Check that:

- ☐ the equipment is erected under the supervision of a competent person and then a pre-check is carried out;

- ☐ anyone using the technique has been expertly trained and is competent;

- ☐ safe descent does not depend upon a single suspension point. Wherever possible the main rope and safety rope should be attached to separate suspension points;

- ☐ all the equipment is checked carefully before each use and maintained to a high standard;

- ☐ any tools which are needed for the work are attached to the operator with suitable ropes or chains, so that they cannot be dropped; and

- ☐ where a risk of dropped tools or falling materials remains the area beneath the work should be fenced off or protected by fans, covered walkways or similar.

See also the general advice on mobile and suspended access equipment (page 34).

Safety harnesses

Providing a safe place of work and system of work to prevent falls should always be the first consideration. However, there may be circumstances in which it is not practicable for all or any of the requirements for guard rails etc to be provided (for example, where guard rails are taken down for short periods to land materials) where people may still approach an open edge from which they would be liable to fall 2 m or more, other forms of protection will be needed. In some cases a suitably attached harness and temporary horizontal lifeline could allow safe working.

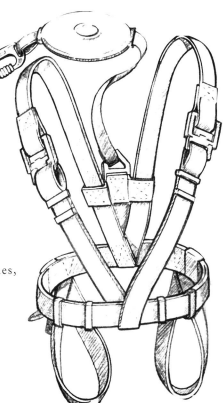

When using harnesses and temporary horizontal lifelines, remember:

- ☐ harnesses and lanyards are made of man-made fibres and as such are prone to degradation

A typical safety harness with leg and shoulder straps. Where a full harness such as this is not used, the maximum possible free-fall distance should not exceed 0.6 m. The lanyard to this harness is also fitted with a shock absorber.

by sunlight, chemicals etc. It is important to carry out tactile pre-use checks daily, in good light, before taking harnesses and lanyards into use. If there is the slightest doubt about a harness or the lanyard, do not use it. Faults can be noticed by discolouration, little tears and nicks, grittiness to touch etc.

☐ a harness will not prevent a fall - it can only minimise the risk of injury if there is a fall. The person who falls may be injured by the impact load to the body when the line goes tight or when they strike against parts of the structure during the fall. An energy absorber fitted to the energy-absorbing lanyard can reduce the risk of injury from impact loads;

☐ minimise free-fall distance. Keep your anchor as high as posssible, thus reducing fall distances.

☐ consider how to recover anyone who does fall;

☐ anyone who needs to attach themselves should be able to do so from a safe position. They need to be able to attach themselves before they move into a position where they are relying on the protection provided by the harness;

☐ the energy-absorbing lanyard should be attached above the wearer where possible. Extra free movement can be provided by using running temporary horizontal lifelines or inertia reels. Any attachment point must be capable of withstanding the impact load in the event of a fall - expert advice may be needed;

☐ to ensure that there is an adequate fall height to allow the system to deploy and arrest the fall;

☐ a twin lanyard may be necessary in some cases where the wearer needs to move about. A twin lanyard allows the wearer to clip on one lanyard in a different position before unclipping the other lanyard;

☐ installation of equipment to which harnesses will be fixed, eg a suitable anchor, must be supervised by a suitably qualified person; and

☐ make sure everyone who uses a harness knows how to check, wear and adjust it before use and how to connect themselves to the structure or safety line as appropriate. Each day, harnesses and lanyards need to be inspected visually, before they are used, for signs of abrasion, tears or general wear and tear. They should be thoroughly examined periodically, and these examinations should be carried out at least every six months.

Ladders

Ladders are best used as a means of getting to a workplace. They should only be used as a workplace for short-term work. They are only suitable for light work.

If ladders are to be used, make sure:

☐   the work only requires one hand to be used;

☐   the work can be reached without stretching;

☐   the ladder can be fixed to prevent slipping; and

☐   a good handhold is available.

Ladder stays can provide additional security.

However, this kind of work can still be dangerous - many ladder accidents happen during work lasting less than 30 minutes. The longer the ladder, the more problems there are in using it safely. It gets harder to handle, is more difficult to foot effectively and it flexes more in use. Make certain there is no other better means of access before using a ladder. Also remember that if people have to use a ladder in several places, which requires them to constantly move the ladder, it is possible that carelessness will creep in.

In order to use a ladder safely, the person should be able to reach the work from a position 1 m below the top of the ladder.

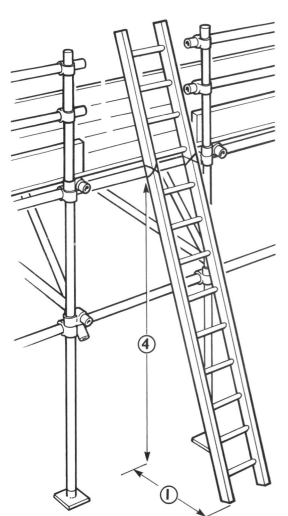

Many accidents result from using ladders for a job when a tower scaffold or mobile access platform would have been safer and more efficient.

Make sure light tools are carried in a shoulder bag or holster attached to a belt so that both hands are free for climbing. Heavy or bulky loads should not be carried up or down ladders - a gin wheel or other lifting equipment should be used instead (see pages 66 to 68).

For safe use the ladder needs to be strong enough for the job and in good condition:

☐   check the stiles are not damaged, buckled or warped, no rungs are cracked or missing and any safety feet are not missing;

This ladder is securely tied to prevent slipping. It is correctly angled (one out for every four up) and extends above the working platform to allow people to get on and off safely.

☐ do not use makeshift or home-made ladders or carry out makeshift repairs to a damaged ladder;

☐ do not use painted ladders, as the paint may hide faults;

☐ ladders made for DIY use may not be strong enough for site work and are best avoided;

☐ DO NOT attempt to repair ladders.

Check the ladder is secure. More than half of the accidents involving ladders happen because the ladder was not prevented from falling or slipping. Ladders are only safe when they rest on a firm, level surface. Do not place them on loose bricks or packing. They should also be secured by rope or other suitable stabilisation devices. Such devices must ensure that the ladder does not:

• run sideways; or

• slide away from the wall.

Also, make sure:

☐ the ladder is angled to minimise the risk of slipping outwards; as a rule of thumb the ladder needs to be 'one out for every four up';

This ladder is placed on a board to prevent it sinking into soft ground and tied to stop it slipping.

☐ the top of the ladder rests against a solid surface; ladders should not rest on fragile or other insecure materials such as cement sheet, or plastic guttering;

☐ both feet of the ladder are on a firm footing and cannot slip;

☐ if the ladder is more than 3 m long, or used as a way to and from a workplace, it is secured from falling. This will usually be by fixing at the top, or sometimes the base;

☐ if the ladder cannot be fixed, a second person foots the ladder while it is being used (this also applies while the ladder is being fixed);

☐ the ladder extends a sufficient height (about 1 m) above any landing place where people will get on and off it unless some other adequate handhold is available; and

☐ where ladders are used in a run measuring a vertical distance of more than 9 m, suitable landing areas or platforms are provided. The only exception to this relates to some steeplejacks' ladders which may not have landing places this often. Nevertheless, provide as many landing places as possible.

Step-ladders

Step-ladders provide a free-standing means of access, but they require careful use. They are not designed for any degree of side loading and are relatively easily overturned. Avoid over-reaching. People have been killed getting down from workplaces such as loft spaces when they have stepped onto the top step of a step-ladder which has then overturned. The top step of a step-ladder should not be worked from unless it has been designed for this purpose.

Protection against falling materials

The risk of falling materials causing injury should be minimised by keeping platforms clear of loose materials. In addition, provide a way of preventing materials or other objects rolling, or being kicked, off the edges of platforms. This may be done with toe boards, solid barriers, brick guards, or similar at open edges. If the scaffold is erected in a public place, nets, fans or covered walkways may be needed to give extra protection for people who may be passing below. High-visibility barrier netting is not suitable for use as a fall prevention device.

Demolition, dismantling and structural alteration

Demolition and dismantling are high risk activities. Workers are injured in falls from edges and through openings and fragile materials. Workers and passers-by can be injured by the premature and uncontrolled collapse of structures or parts of structures and by flying debris. High levels of dust, noise and other site contamination are also significant problems which need to be considered and controlled when planning any demolition work.

Brickguards should be positioned so that they are prevented from moving outwards by the toe board.

Safe demolition requires planning. The key to developing a safe system of work for demolition and dismantling is choosing a work method which keeps people as far away as possible from the risks. Proposed working methods may be best detailed in a health and safety method statement (see page 95). Everyone involved in the work needs to know what precautions are to be taken. They should be supervised so that these precautions are put into practice.

It is essential that demolition is planned and carried out under the supervision of a competent person. Supervisors should have knowledge of the particular type of demolition being carried out, its hazards and how to control them. In particular, they should understand and follow any demolition method statement and know of any particular demolition sequence required to avoid accidental collapse of the structure.

Before work starts, the site should be surveyed for hazardous material and structural condition. Consider the following matters:

☐ can a method which keeps people away from the demolition be used, for example, using a high-reach machine or a crane with a ball? Cabs of machines should be protected to safeguard drivers from falling materials;

☐ will the sequence of demolition make the structure itself, or any nearby buildings or structures unstable? Is temporary propping required? The advice of a structural engineer may be needed;

☐ will the method of work make the floors, walls or any other part of the structure, support the weight of removed material building up on them or the weight of machines, for example, skid-steer loaders used to clear the surcharge? Again, expert advice may be needed;

☐ are there still any live services? Gas, electricity and water services need to be dealt with;

☐ is there any left-over contamination from previous use of the building, for example, acids from industrial processes? Has all the asbestos in the building been identified, such as asbestos on pipework, boilers and wall and ceiling panels (see page 77-79)? Have microbiological hazards in old hospitals or medical buildings been identified? Hazardous materials will normally need to be removed and disposed of safely before demolition starts to prevent the spread of contamination. Precautions needed for working with hazardous materials are set out in pages 73-76.

Anyone who is not involved in the work should be kept away. Create an exclusion zone around the work area, which should be clearly marked, where necessary, by barriers or hoardings. Do not allow materials to fall into any area where people are working or passing through. Fans, or other protection such as covered walkways, may be needed to provide protection where materials can fall.

Fire is also a risk, especially where hot work is being carried out, so make sure the precautions (see pages 14 to 16) are in place.

The CDM Regulations apply to all demolition and dismantling work (see page 99).

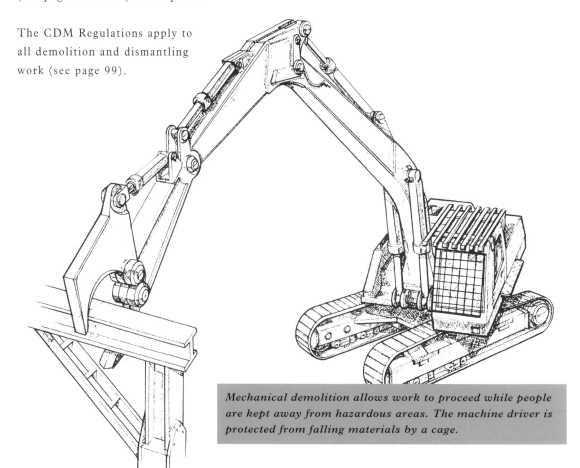

Mechanical demolition allows work to proceed while people are kept away from hazardous areas. The machine driver is protected from falling materials by a cage.

Steel erection

When designing and planning for the erection of steel frames, the first consideration should be to eliminate or reduce the need to work at height. Where work at height cannot be avoided, mobile platforms (see MEWPs, page 35) or tower scaffolds (see pages 32 to 33) or other suitable working platforms should be used for access for bolting-up and similar operations. Make sure the ground is suitable before work starts, to allow safe use of mobile platforms or tower scaffolds and safe standing for a crane.

Steel erection requires careful planning and execution - it is best left to specialists. There is also much potential to reduce risks during design and planning by, for example:

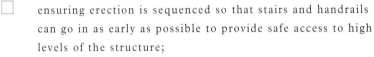

- [ ] ensuring erection is sequenced so that stairs and handrails can go in as early as possible to provide safe access to high levels of the structure;

- [ ] designing connection joints to make bolting-up easy;

- [ ] adding bracing into the design to ensure integral stability of the structure through all stages of erection;

- [ ] ensuring adequate information is passed on to alert erectors about special sequences which need to be followed to ensure stability.

The main hazards to be controlled on site are:

- falls when working at height;

- erectors being hit or knocked off the steel by moving steel members or decking packs being craned into position;

- the structure collapsing before it is fully braced;

- materials dropping onto people working below;

- the manual lifting of heavy steel members, causing back and other strains and injuries; and

- cranes overturning.

Whenever possible erectors should work from an independent platform. If it is unavoidable that erectors have to work on the steel, beams should either be straddled, or if the web is very deep, crabbed. Erectors should wear a full harness attatched to either the steel or a running line (see page 39).

Before work starts, plan safe working methods:

- [ ] plan for good access onto the site and proper standing areas for delivery vehicles, cranes, mobile work platforms and tower scaffolds;

- [ ] arrange for materials to be stored safely;

- [ ] programme work to make sure other trades do not have to work beneath the erectors, so avoiding the risk of them being injured by dropped materials;

☐ arrange for safe working at height using mobile work platforms, tower scaffolds or another form of independent access if possible;

☐ if work cannot be done from a MEWP or other platform, erectors may have to work from the steel. Where workers are working from the steel, erectors must wear a harness and lanyard. In many cases, this needs to be a twin lanyard. When the safe system of work relies on harnesses, a system must be in place to rescue a person who may fall and be left suspended from their harness;

☐ walking on the top flange of steel beam is dangerous - make it clear that workers must not do it;

☐ check temporary bracing to ensure stability has been provided - consult the frame designer or a structural engineer; and

☐ agree a safety method statement and ensure it is followed.

Workers fall not only during the erection of the frame, but also when decking sheets are being handled. People can fall:

• during the landing and splitting of decking packs;

• when decking sheets are being moved around the frame;

• during the laying of decking sheets; and

• from edges of decked areas (including leading edges).

A manlock girder grip device can provide a secure temporary attachment to the steel.

To prevent these falls:

☐ assess the type of work being done (this will include the height of the building and height between floors etc) and plan a safe system of work to prevent falls. This may entail positioning decking sheets from mobile access platforms or tower scaffolds. In many cases, a safe system may require the use of nets under the working position to mitigate the effect of falls from the leading edge. Where nets are not suitable, it will be necessary to use harnesses attached to a suitable anchorage.

☐ position guard rails at all fixed edges and openings; and

☐ where possible, store and split packs of decking sheets at ground level or on a previously decked area of the frame provided with suitable guard rails.

The hazards associated with the laying of decking and the necessary precautions are similar to those required for safe working during industrial roofing. See pages 52 to 53 for further details.

See the safety harnesses section, page 39.

Formwork and reinforced concrete work

The main risks are:

- people falling during steel-fixing and erection of formwork;

- collapse of the formwork or falsework;

- materials falling while striking the formwork;

- manual handling of shutters, reinforcing bars etc;

- being struck by the concrete skip;

- silica dust from scabbling operations;

- arm and back strain for steel-fixers;

- cement burns from wet concrete.

Many of these risks can be reduced or removed by design and careful planning of the formwork. For example:

☐ Designers should consider the manual handling risks when detailing size and length of the reinforcing bar.

☐ Fixing reinforcement steel in prefabricated sections in factory conditions and craning it into position. Work can be done on work benches to reduce the need for bending down.

☐ Using formwork systems that have edge protection and access designed in.

☐ Minimising the need for scabbling by using retarders.

☐ Using concrete pumps instead of crane and skip.

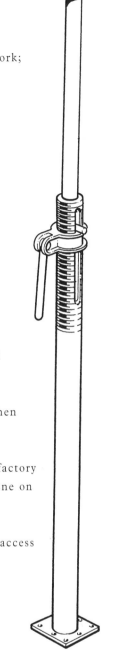

Make sure:

☐ a method statement has been agreed before work starts and that it is followed;

☐ guard rails or other suitable barriers to prevent falls are put in place as work progresses;

☐ workers have safe access to the work - it is not safe to stand on primary or other open timbers;

Adjustable props. The end plate should be flat and square to the tube. Both tubular sections should be straight and undented. The correct pin should be in place. The collar should be free to move over threads which are clean and lubricated. When using adjustable props, they should be vertical and not over-extended in length (the greater the extension, the less load they can carry). The load that a prop has to carry must be known so that enough props can be used. Where several props are used together, they should to be braced together.

A tower scaffold can provide safe access to columns - it is not safe to climb the formwork itself.

☐ a ladder or a tower scaffold is used for access;

☐ ladders are tied - climbing up vertical sections of reinforcement or the wedges of column forms should not be permitted;

☐ equipment is in good order before use. Do not use substitutes for the manufacturer's pins in adjustable props;

☐ the formwork, falsework and temporary supports are checked, properly tied, footed, braced and supported before loading, and before pouring walls or columns;

- [ ] workers are protected from wet concrete (provide gloves and wellington boots) and silica dust (provide respirators or avoid the need to scabble by using a retarder);

- [ ] loads are spread as evenly as possible on the temporary structure - do not place large loads of timber, reinforcing bars or wet concrete in a localised area - spread loads evenly;

- [ ] it is known when back-propping is required and how soon the new structure can be loaded; and

- [ ] there is a planned safe striking procedure.

Also see the sections on working platforms and prevention of falls (page 30), and safety harnesses (page 39).

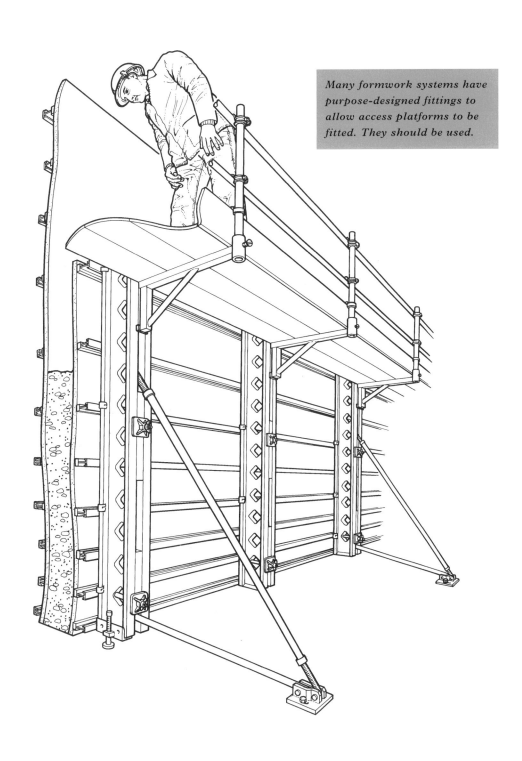

Many formwork systems have purpose-designed fittings to allow access platforms to be fitted. They should be used.

Roof work

Almost one in five workers killed in construction accidents are doing roof work. Most of these are specialist roofers, but some are simply involved in maintaining and cleaning roofs. Some of these workers die after falling off the edges of flat and sloping roofs.

Many other workers die after falling through fragile materials. Many roof assemblies are, or can become, fragile. Asbestos cement, fibreglass and plastic generally become more fragile with age. Steel sheets may rust. Sheets on poorly repaired roofs might not be properly supported.

DANGER Fragile roof

Any of these materials could give way without warning. Do not trust any sheeted roof. Do not stand directly on any of them. On a fragile roof, never try to walk along the line of the roof bolts above the purlins, or along the roof ridge, as the sheets can still crack and give way.

Roof openings and fragile rooflights are an extra hazard. Some rooflights are difficult to see in certain light conditions and others may be hidden by paint. Protection from falling through openings and fragile rooflights can be provided by barriers or with covers which are secured or labelled with a warning.

A scaffold platform at eaves level provides safe access for work on a pitched roof.

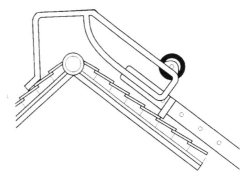

On fragile roofs, the work has to be carefully planned to prevent falls through the roof. If access onto the roof cannot be avoided, working platforms to spread the load (or other proprietary access system) will be necessary. These should be used with edge protection or harnesses (if a suitable anchorage position is not available a life line system may have to be installed).

On sloping roofs, purpose-made roof ladders or boards to spread the weight of workers and materials will be required.

Guard rails and toe boards or suitable barriers erected at the edge or eaves level of a roof are usually needed to stop people and materials from falling off. If work is going to be done on any roof, make sure there is:

☐ safe access onto and off the roof, for example, a general access or tower scaffold;

☐ a safe means of moving across the roof, for example, suitable roof ladders; and

☐ a safe means of working on the roof - a guard railed platform (for example, a scaffold or a MEWP).

Do not throw materials such as old slates, tiles etc from the roof or scaffold - someone may be passing by. Use enclosed debris chutes or lower the debris in containers (see page 89).

Roof ladders can allow safe access for small repairs. It is particularly important to tie the access ladder in a secure position to avoid it slipping when stepping between it and the roof ladder.

Industrial roofing

This work involves all the hazards already mentioned. In addition, falls from the 'leading edge' need to be prevented. Leading edges are created as new roof sheets are laid, or old ones are removed. Falls from these edges should be prevented as well as falls from roof edges and through fragile materials. Fragile and lightweight materials, such as liner trays which will buckle and give way under the weight of a person, can also be a problem and should be protected.

Work at the leading edge requires careful planning to develop a safe system of work. Nets are the preferred method for reducing the risk of injury from falls at the leading edge, as they provide protection to everyone on the roof. The erection of nets should be carried out by trained riggers.

Stagings, fitted with guard rails or suitable barriers and toe boards, in advance of the leading edge can provide protection in some circumstances. However, these will need to be used in conjunction with harnesses attached to a suitable fixing. Close supervision of this system of work will be required as it is difficult for harnesses to remain clipped on at all times throughout the work activity.

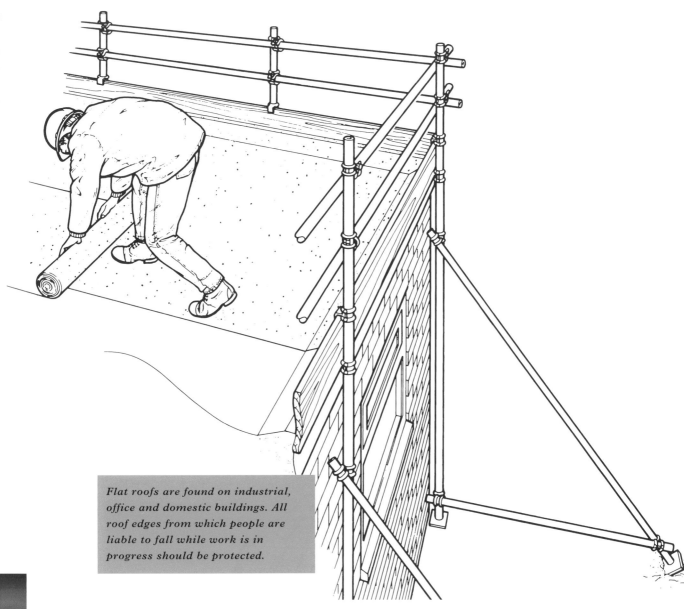

Flat roofs are found on industrial, office and domestic buildings. All roof edges from which people are liable to fall while work is in progress should be roofed.

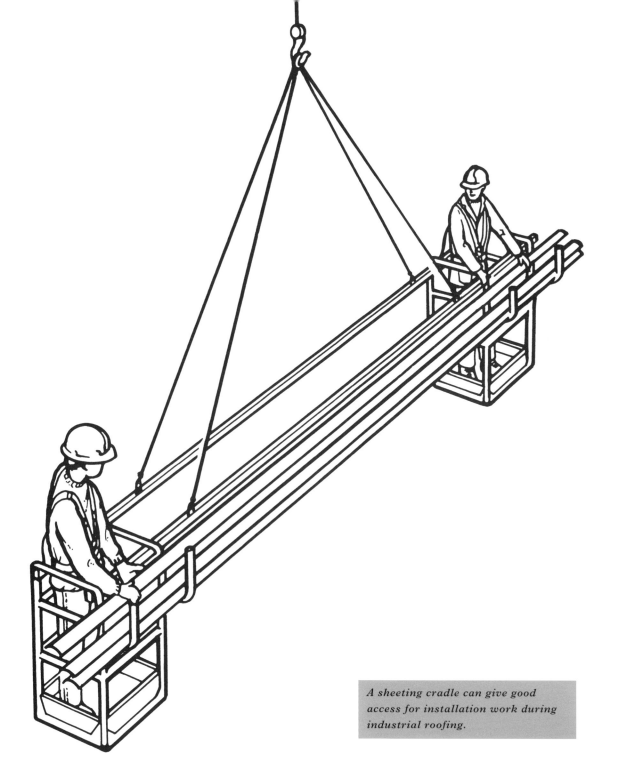

A sheeting cradle can give good access for installation work during industrial roofing.

When developing a safe system of work, also consider:

☐ how the first sheets will be laid - a separate platform may be required (a pack of roof sheets is not a safe working platform) - and how hip ends and other special details are to be fitted; and

☐ how sheets will be raised to roof level - decide whether lifting machinery such as an inclined hoist can be used. This will eliminate unnecessary risks when placing packs of sheets on the roof supports or when breaking open packs spread over the roof supports.

For more information on all aspects of roof work read *Health and safety in roof work*.[15]

GROUNDWORK

Every year people are killed or seriously injured while working in excavations. Many are killed or injured by collapses and falling materials, some are killed or injured when they contact buried underground services. Groundwork has to be properly planned and carried out to prevent accidents.

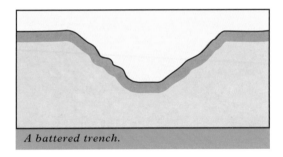

A battered trench.

Excavations

Before digging any trenches, pits, tunnels, or other excavations, decide what temporary support will be required and plan the precautions that are going to be taken against:

- collapse of the sides;

- materials falling onto people working in the excavation;

- people and vehicles falling into the excavation;

- undermining nearby structures etc;

- underground services;

- water inflow; and

- premature removal of support.

Make sure the equipment and precautions needed such as trench sheets, props, baulks etc are available on site before work starts. If information such as results of soil tests or trial holes is available, it may provide useful data on conditions likely to be found on site which can assist planning. Put the precautions into practice.

Collapse of the sides or roof

☐ Prevent the sides from collapsing by battering them to a safe angle or supporting them with sheeting or proprietary support systems. Take similar precautions to prevent the face from collapsing.

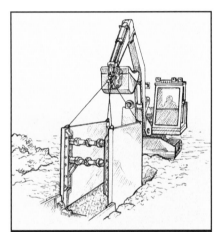

A range of proprietary trench boxes and hydraulic wallings allow trench supports to be put in place without requiring people to enter the excavation.

Install support without delay as the excavation progresses. Never work ahead of the support. The work should be directed by a competent supervisor. Give the workers clear instructions.

A competent person who fully understands the dangers and necessary precautions should inspect the excavation at the start of each shift. Excavations should also be inspected after any event that may have affected their strength or stability, or after a fall of rock or earth. A record of the inspections will be required (see section on inspections, pages 21 to 23). Put right immediately any faults that are found.

Materials falling into excavations

Do not store excavated spoil and other materials or park plant and vehicles close to the sides of excavations. The extra loadings from spoil, vehicles, etc can make the sides of excavations more likely to collapse. Loose materials may fall from spoil heaps, etc into the excavation. A scaffold board used as a toe board and fixed along the outside of the trench sheets will provide extra protection against loose materials falling. Hard hats will protect those working in the excavation from small pieces of materials falling either from above, or from the sides of the excavation.

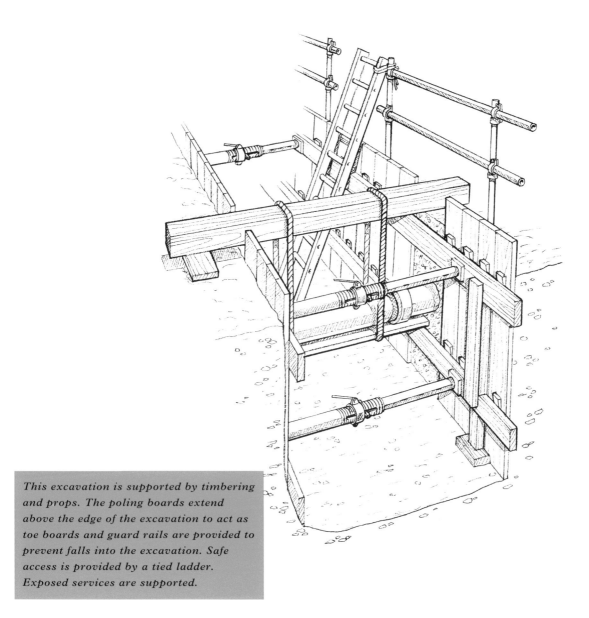

This excavation is supported by timbering and props. The poling boards extend above the edge of the excavation to act as toe boards and guard rails are provided to prevent falls into the excavation. Safe access is provided by a tied ladder. Exposed services are supported.

People and vehicles falling into excavations

☐ Prevent people from falling by guarding excavations. Edges of excavations more than 2 m deep should be protected with substantial barriers where people are liable to fall into them (see page 26). All excavations in public places should be suitably fenced off to prevent members of the public approaching them (see pages 88 to 91).

☐ Prevent vehicles from falling into excavations by keeping them out of the area. Vehicles passing close to the edges of excavations may also overload the sides, leading to collapse. Where necessary, use baulks or barriers to keep vehicles away from excavated edges. Baulks and barriers are best painted or marked to make sure they can be seen by drivers.

☐ Where vehicles have to tip materials into excavations, prevent them from over-running into the excavation by using stop-blocks. The sides of the excavation may need extra support.

Undermining nearby structures

☐ Make sure excavations do not undermine the footings of scaffolds, buried services or the foundations of nearby buildings or walls. Many garden or boundary walls have very shallow foundations which are easily undermined by even small trenches, causing the wall to collapse onto those working in the trench. Before digging starts, decide if extra support for the structure is needed. Surveys of the foundations and the advice of a structural engineer may be required.

Other aspects of excavation safety

☐ Ensure there is good ladder access or other ways of getting in and out of the excavation safely.

☐ Consider hazardous fumes - do not use petrol or diesel engines in excavations without making arrangements for the fumes to be ducted safely away or providing for forced ventilation. Do not site petrol or diesel-engined equipment such as generators or compressors in, or near the edge of an excavation; exhaust gases can collect and accumulate. For information about fumes in confined spaces, including excavations, see pages 59 to 61.

For further information on excavation work, read *Health and safety in excavations: be safe and shore.*[16]

Underground services

Underground services can be easily damaged during excavation work. If the proper precautions are not taken, it is all too easy for workers to hit these services, resulting in risk:

- to themselves and anyone nearby from the heat, flame and molten metal given off when an electricity cable is struck; from escaping gas when a gas pipe is hit; or from flooding of the excavation when a water pipe is damaged; and

- from the interruption of services to hospitals, emergency services etc.

Before work starts, service plans should be obtained. Use the service plans to see whether the place intended for digging will involve working near buried underground services. Look out for signs of services such as manholes, valve covers, street-lights etc. Check for pipes and cables before starting to dig.

Contact with services can be avoided by proper planning and execution. A safe system of work depends upon the use of:

- cable or other service plans;

- cable and service locators; and

- safe digging practices.

Whenever possible, keep excavations well away from existing services.

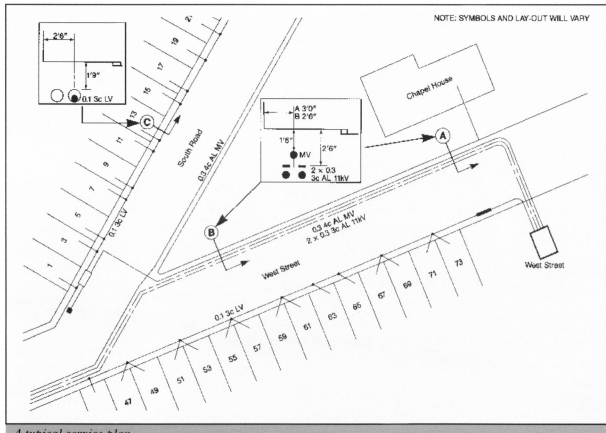

A typical service plan.

Before digging, make sure that:

☐ all workers involved in the digging know about safe digging practice and emergency procedures and that they are properly supervised;

☐ the locator is used to trace as accurately as possible the actual line of any pipe or cable or to confirm that there are no pipes or cables in the way and the ground has been marked accordingly;

☐ there is an emergency plan to deal with damage to cables or pipes. Have a system for notifying the service owner in all circumstances. In the case of gas pipe damage, ban smoking and naked flames. Carry out evacuation whenever necessary (this may include people in nearby properties likely to be affected by leaks). Erect suitable signs to warn everyone of the danger. See also Emergency procedures, pages 12 to 14.

Excavate using safe digging practice:

☐ keep a careful watch for evidence of pipes or cables during digging and repeat checks with the locator. If unidentified services are found, stop work until further checks can be made to confirm it is safe to proceed;

☐ hand dig trial holes to confirm the position of the pipes or cables. This is particularly important in the case of plastic pipes which cannot be detected by normal locating equipment.

☐ hand dig near buried pipes or cables or use air-powered excavation devices. Use spades and shovels rather than picks and forks which are more likely to pierce cables. It is particularly important that you:

• do not use handheld power tools within 0.5 m of the indicated position of an electricity cable;

• do not use an excavator to excavate within 0.5 m of a gas pipe.

☐ treat all pipes or cables as 'live' unless it is known otherwise. What looks like a rusty pipe may be conduit containing a live cable. Do not break or cut into any service until its identity is certain and it is known that it has been made safe;

☐ support services once they are exposed to prevent them from being damaged, and make sure that they are not used as hand or footholds when people are getting in and out of the trench;

☐ report any suspected damage to services;

☐ backfill around pipes or cables with fine material. Backfill which is properly compacted, particularly under cast or rigid pipes, prevents settlement which could cause damage at a later date;

☐ once new services have been laid, update the plans.

For further information on avoiding danger from underground services see HSE's guidance *Avoiding danger from underground services.*[17]

WORKING IN CONFINED SPACES

Not knowing the dangers of confined spaces has led to the deaths of many workers. Often those killed include not only those working in the confined space but also those who, not properly equipped, try to rescue them. Work in such spaces requires skilled and trained people to ensure safety. If work cannot be avoided in a confined space, it will often be safer to bring in a specialist for the job.

Why is a confined space dangerous?

Air in the confined space is made unbreathable either by poisonous gases and fumes or by lack of oxygen. There is not enough natural ventilation to keep the air fit to breathe. In some cases the gases may be flammable, so there may also be a fire or explosion risk.

Working space may be restricted, bringing workers into close contact with other hazards such as moving machinery, electricity or steam vents and pipes. The entrance to a confined space, for example, a manhole, may make escape or rescue in an emergency more difficult.

How does it get dangerous?

Some confined spaces are naturally dangerous, for example, because of:

- gas build-up in sewers and manholes and pits connected to them;

- gases leaking into trenches and pits in contaminated land such as old refuse tips and old gas works;

- rust inside tanks and vessels which eats up the oxygen;

- liquids and slurries which can suddenly fill the space or release gases into it when disturbed;

- chemical reaction between some soils and air causing oxygen depletion or the action of ground water on chalk and limestone producing carbon dioxide.

Some places are made dangerous by vapours from the work done in them. Keep hazards out of confined spaces. Do not use petrol or diesel engines because exhaust gases are poisonous. Paints, glues etc may give off hazardous vapours. Ensure the confined space has enough ventilation to make the air fit to breathe. Mechanical ventilation might be needed.

How to work safely

There should be a safe system of work for operations inside confined spaces. Everyone should know and follow the system. A permit-to-work system may be required.

For safe working, first try to find a way of doing the job without going into the confined space. If entry is essential:

☐ identify what work must be done in the confined space and the hazards involved;

☐ consider if the space could be altered to make it permanently safe or if the work could be changed to make entry to the dangerous area unnecessary;

☐ make sure workers have been trained in the dangers and precautions, including rescue procedures;

☐ make sure the entrance to the space is big enough to allow workers wearing all the necessary equipment to climb in and out easily;

☐ before entry, ventilate the space as much as possible, test the air inside the space and only enter if the test shows it is safe;

☐ after entry, continue to test the air for toxic substances, flammable gases and oxygen deficiency as necessary;

☐ if there is a flammable risk, the space must be ventilated until it is safe. When selecting equipment, remember heat or sparks from electrical or other equipment could ignite flammable vapours, so air-powered tools may be required. The risk from flammable vapours is very high when work is carried out on the tanks of petrol service stations and similar sites. This is work which may be safer left to a specialist contractor;

☐ disturbing deposits and slurries in pipes and tanks may produce extra vapour, resulting in a greater risk, so clear deposits before entry where possible;

☐ if the air inside the space cannot be made fit to breathe because of a toxic risk or lack of oxygen, workers must wear breathing apparatus;

Where necessary use a meter to check air quality before entering a confined space and to monitor the air while work proceeds.

Self-contained breathing apparatus (SCBA) - open circuit compressed air type. People wearing this and other types of breathing apparatus, should be trained and competent before beginning work.

- never try to 'sweeten' the air in a confined space with oxygen as this can produce a fire and explosion risk;

- workers inside the confined space should wear rescue harnesses, with lifelines attached, which run back to a point outside the confined space;

- someone should be outside to keep watch and to communicate with anyone inside, raise the alarm in an emergency and take charge of rescue procedures if it becomes necessary. It is essential those outside the space know what to do in an emergency. They need to know how to use breathing apparatus if they are to effect a rescue. See also emergency procedures, pages 12 to 14.

For further information on working in confined spaces, read *Safe work in confined spaces*[18] and see pages 73 to 76.

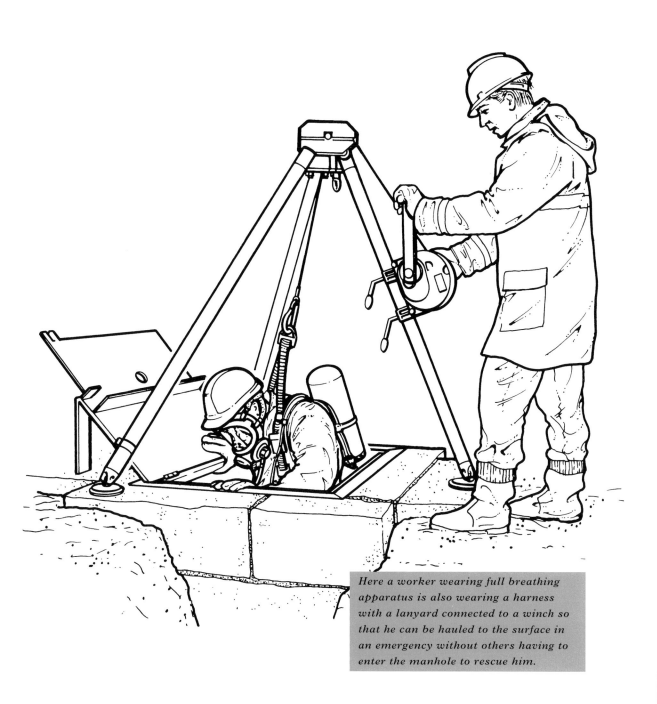

Here a worker wearing full breathing apparatus is also wearing a harness with a lanyard connected to a winch so that he can be hauled to the surface in an emergency without others having to enter the manhole to rescue him.

PREVENTION OF DROWNING

There is a risk of drowning when people work beside or above water or have to pass near or across it on their way to or from their workplace. People can also drown in other liquids such as slurries in lagoons, foodstuffs in open vats in food processing works and solutions of chemicals in factories. This includes any fine material such as sand or grain, or surfaces that have a high percentage of water in them such as slurry or estuarine mud.

A series of measure can be taken to significantly reduce the risk of drowning. These include:

☐   diverting or reducing rates of flow in channels where possible by closing sluice gates etc;

☐   barriers to stop people from falling into the water or other liquid. In most cases guard rails and toe boards or a similar barrier will be needed at open edges to ensure people cannot fall into the water or liquid. In factories and some other locations it may be possible to cover the surface of the container or to drain it;

☐   **raising the alarm**

- When working over or near to water there should be means to raise the alarm if any has fallen into the water;

Rescue and safety equipment must always be easily available and in good condition

☐ **Lifejackets**

- Providing life jackets to those at risk. Lifejackets should ideally be auto-inflating. Ensure anyone who needs to wear a life preserver is trained in its use and what to do in an emergency.

☐ **Throw lines and grab lines**

- A line can be tensioned across the river downstream of the work site to act as a safety feature. This line should be tensioned across the river so that it runs at 45 degrees to the flow, with the most downstream end to the bank from which easiest access can be made. This allows the swimmer as they hit the line to be washed to the downstream end. Do not tension the line at 90 degrees to the flow.

- A throw line should not be tied to anything. For use in moving water it needs to be 8-12 mm diameter for ease of handling, brightly coloured and able to float to avoid entanglement on the river bed.

- Do not tie the line to anything. If the force is too much to hold, the rescuer should walk down the bank recovering or releasing the line to avoid the possibility of the rescuer being pulled into the river. A tied or snagged line may have the effect of submerging the person in the water if the current is fast.

☐ **Rescue boats**

- Suitable rescue boat or boats, with a competent operator, may be needed. This is particularly important when people may fall into the sea or flowing water. The boat should be designed so that it is easy to pull a casualty from the water into the boat. The type of rescue boat depends on the circumstances of the work and type of water and any currents. In fast flowing water two people may be necessary to effect a rescue, one to manoeuvre the boat and the other to pull the casualty from the water.

To be effective, these precautions need to be maintained. People need to know what to do in an emergency and how to raise the alarm.

Where people can fall into other materials which flow and into which they can sink and suffocate, such as fine sands or grain, similar means of prevention and rescue may be required.

People are also at risk of drowning when they must travel by boat to reach their workplace, for example, for certain work at docks, in rivers, at dams and on islands. Any boat used to convey people by water to or from a place of work should:

- be of suitable construction;

- be properly maintained;

- be under the control of a competent person; and

- not be overcrowded or overloaded.

See also Emergency procedures, pages 12-14.

MOVING, LIFTING AND HANDLING LOADS

Many construction workers are killed or seriously injured during lifting operations because of accidents such as:

- cranes overturning;

- material falling from hoists; and

- gin wheels collapsing.

Many more suffer long-term injury because they regularly lift or carry items which are heavy or awkward to handle, for example:

- blocklayers lifting dense concrete blocks;

- paviours laying slabs; and

- labourers lifting and carrying bagged products, such as cement and aggregates.

Plan all material handling to avoid the risk of injury. Where possible, avoid people having to lift materials at all. Provide mechanical handling aids wherever possible to avoid manual handling injuries. Make sure that all equipment used for lifting is in good condition and used by trained and competent workers.

Plan for material handling:

☐ before the job starts, decide what sort of material handling is going to take place and what equipment will be needed;

☐ avoid double handling - it increases risks and is inefficient;

☐ make sure that any equipment is delivered to the site in good time and that the site has been prepared for it;

☐ ensure the equipment is set up and operated only by trained and experienced workers;

☐ co-ordinate site activities so that those involved in lifting operations do not endanger other workers and vice versa;

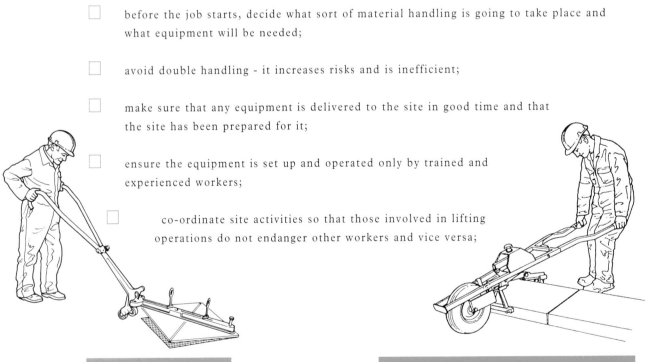

A manhole cover lifter.

A paving slab and general purpose-handler.

- [ ] do not stand under loads being lifted;

- [ ] arrange for the equipment to be regularly inspected and thoroughly examined at relevant time periods by a competent person. Make sure reports of through examinations and records of inspections are kept. The Lifting Operations and Lifting Equipment Regulations 1998 (see page 99) give details of what has to be documented.

Manual handling

Lifting and moving loads by hand is one of the most common causes of injury at work. Many manual handling injuries result from repeated operations, but even one bad lift can cause a lifetime of pain and disability. The Manual Handling Operations Regulations 1992 require employers to avoid the need to carry out manual handling which creates a risk of injury. Where avoidance is not reasonably practicable, employers have to make an assessment, reduce the risk of injury as far as reasonably practicable and provide information about the weight of loads.

When manual handling is necessary, prevent injury by:

- [ ] avoiding unnecessary handling;

This gin wheel is located by two clips to prevent it sliding out of position.

- [ ] identifying, before work is begun, operations which involve either lifting heavy or awkward loads or repetitive lifting operations. Find ways of either avoiding the operation altogether, or using mechanical aids to minimise the amount of manual handling;

- [ ] sharing heavy or awkward loads which have to be lifted by hand. Remember, some workers are stronger than others and no one is immune from injury;

- [ ] positioning loads by machine and planning to reduce the height from which they have to be lifted and the distance over which they have to be carried;

- [ ] training workers in safe lifting techniques and sensible handling of loads;

- [ ] not requiring anyone on their own to lift building blocks weighing more than 20 kgs;

- [ ] ordering bagged materials in small easily handled sizes where possible; most building products are now available in 25 kg bags.

Anyone injuring their back at work should be encouraged to report the injury, get early medical attention and return only gradually to handling duties.

For further information on lifting building blocks, see HSE's information sheet *Handling heavy building blocks*.[19] Guidance on the Manual Handling Operations Regulations is given in *Manual handling*[20] and *Getting to grips with manual handling - a short guide for employers*.[21] Practical solutions to problems are provided in *Backs for the future: Safe manual handling in construction*[22] and *Manual handling: Solutions you can handle*.[23]

Small lifting equipment

Gin wheels and similar equipment provide a very convenient way of raising loads. Though simple pieces of equipment, care is needed when assembling and using them if accidents are to be avoided (see illustration on page 65). If a gin wheel or similar is to be used, make sure it has:

☐ been securely fixed to a secure anchorage, to prevent displacement;

☐ a proper hook designed to prevent displacement of the load or a hook fitted with a safety catch. The safety catch will retain the load in case it snags. Do not use bent reinforcing rods or other makeshift hooks; and

☐ there is a safe working platform from which the hook can be loaded and unloaded.

A hook designed to prevent displacement of the load.

A hook with a safety catch.

Hoists

Select a hoist which is suitable for the site and capable of lifting the loads required. Also:

☐ set the controls up:

• so that the hoist can be operated from one position only, for example, ground level; and

• the operator can see all the landing levels from the operating position.

To prevent people being struck by the

Leaning out to pull in a swivel hoist is hazardous. In this installation a rail which allows access to a wheelbarrow on the hoist platform enables the platform to be pulled in safely.

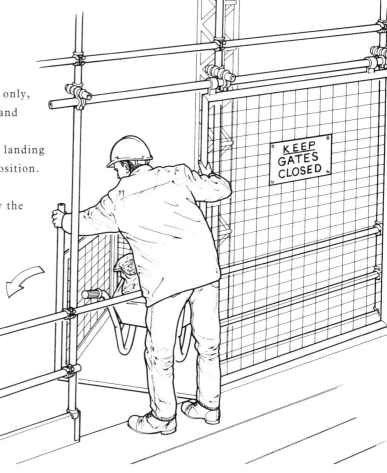

KEEP GATES CLOSED

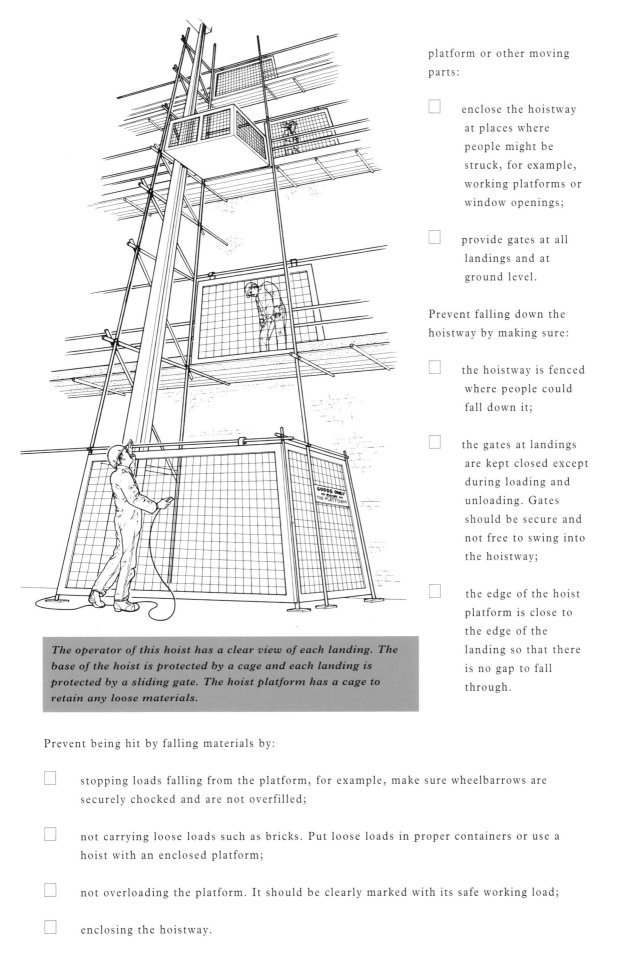

platform or other moving parts:

☐ enclose the hoistway at places where people might be struck, for example, working platforms or window openings;

☐ provide gates at all landings and at ground level.

Prevent falling down the hoistway by making sure:

☐ the hoistway is fenced where people could fall down it;

☐ the gates at landings are kept closed except during loading and unloading. Gates should be secure and not free to swing into the hoistway;

☐ the edge of the hoist platform is close to the edge of the landing so that there is no gap to fall through.

The operator of this hoist has a clear view of each landing. The base of the hoist is protected by a cage and each landing is protected by a sliding gate. The hoist platform has a cage to retain any loose materials.

Prevent being hit by falling materials by:

☐ stopping loads falling from the platform, for example, make sure wheelbarrows are securely chocked and are not overfilled;

☐ not carrying loose loads such as bricks. Put loose loads in proper containers or use a hoist with an enclosed platform;

☐ not overloading the platform. It should be clearly marked with its safe working load;

☐ enclosing the hoistway.

No one should be allowed to ride on a goods hoist. Put up a notice to say so.

Make sure:

☐ the hoist is erected by trained and experienced people following the manufacturer's instructions and properly secured to the supporting structure;

☐ the hoist operator has been trained and is competent;

☐ loads are evenly distributed on the hoist platform;

☐ the hoist is thoroughly examined and tested after erection, substantial alteration or repair and at relevant intervals. Regular checks should be carried out and the results recorded. As a general guide, weekly checks should suffice.

Mobile cranes

Mobile cranes are a versatile, reliable means of lifting on site. However, it is easy to become complacent about their safe use. Complacency can lead to serious accidents. No lift is small enough to be left to chance. Every lift should be planned and carried out by trained, competent people. If no one has the expertise, contract out the work to someone who has. If a lift is going to be carried out, accidents can be avoided by appointing someone (not the driver) with the expertise to take charge. That person will need to plan and co-ordinate the lift as follows:

Planning the lift

☐ Select the right crane for the job. It will need to be:

• able to lift the heaviest load at the required radius with capacity to spare. The maximum load a crane can lift decreases the further the load is from the crane, so a crane rated at 20 tonnes may be needed to lift a 1 tonne load;

• small enough to get on and off the site and to operate within it.

☐ Check that the crane and any lifting accessories have a current thorough examination report.

☐ Make sure a rated capacity indicator (Automatic Safe Load Indicator) is fitted (when the crane is able to lift more than one tonne) and is in good working order.

☐ Make sure the driver is trained and experienced in the operation of the type of crane being used.

☐ Site the crane in a safe place, so that:

• the driver has a clear view;

• it is well away from excavations, and overhead power lines;

• it is on level ground which can take its full weight and its load (timber packing may be needed) - check there are no voids such as drains or basements which could collapse suddenly.

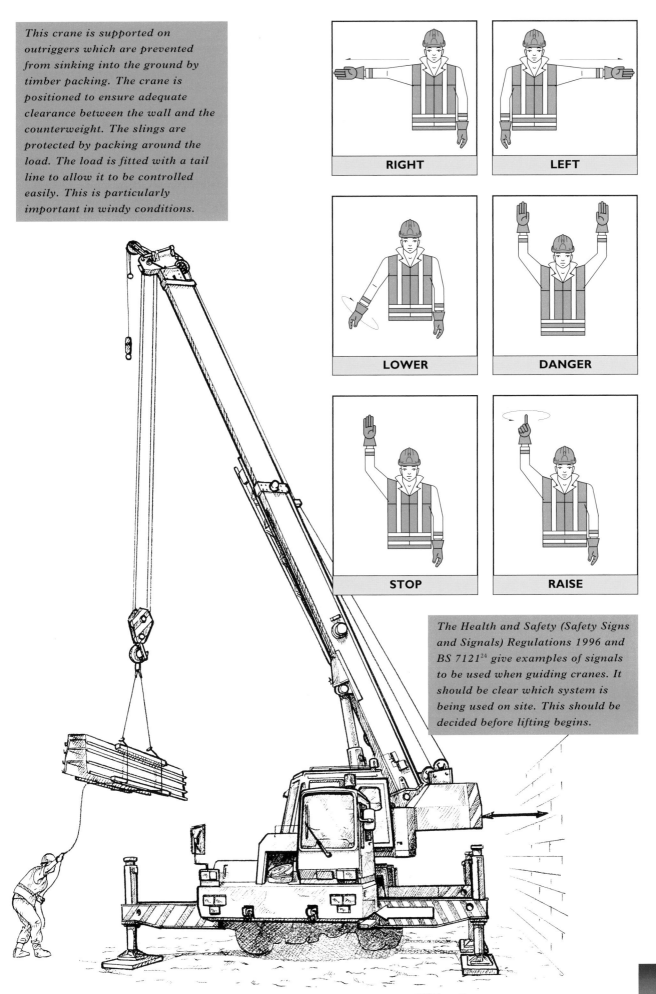

This crane is supported on outriggers which are prevented from sinking into the ground by timber packing. The crane is positioned to ensure adequate clearance between the wall and the counterweight. The slings are protected by packing around the load. The load is fitted with a tail line to allow it to be controlled easily. This is particularly important in windy conditions.

RIGHT

LEFT

LOWER

DANGER

STOP

RAISE

The Health and Safety (Safety Signs and Signals) Regulations 1996 and BS 7121[24] give examples of signals to be used when guiding cranes. It should be clear which system is being used on site. This should be decided before lifting begins.

Co-ordinating the lift

Make sure:

☐ the load is slung by a competent person and that chains and slings of correct strength are used and are in good condition;

☐ the load is properly slung. Chains and slings may be damaged by the load, so packing may be required. The centre of gravity of the load may not be in the middle of the load (this is very common with pieces of plant), causing it to shift or slip out of its slings when it is raised. It is important that loads are slung so that they are in balance with their centre of gravity beneath the hook;

☐ a competent person has been appointed to sling the load. If the driver's view is restricted, provide a banksman or signaller;

☐ there is adequate clearance so that people are not struck or trapped by the load, counterweight or body of the crane. If traps are unavoidable, fence them off;

☐ the crane and the lifting tackle have been checked and maintained as recommended by the manufacturer;

☐ weekly inspections of the crane are made and the results recorded.

For further information on the safe use of mobile cranes on site, see BS 7121.[24]

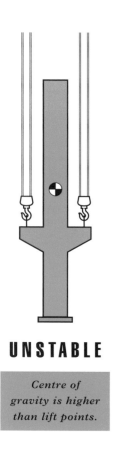

UNSTABLE

Centre of gravity is higher than lift points.

⊕ *Centre of gravity*

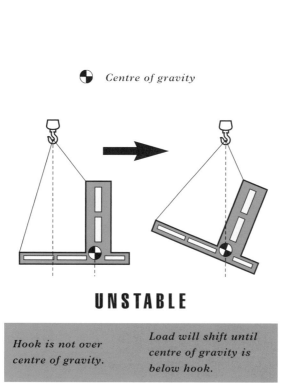

UNSTABLE

Hook is not over centre of gravity.

Load will shift until centre of gravity is below hook.

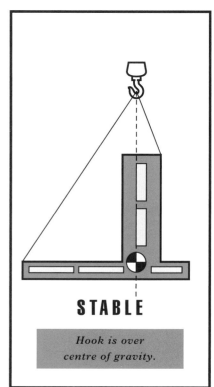

STABLE

Hook is over centre of gravity.

SITE VEHICLES AND MOBILE PLANT

Workers are killed every year on construction sites by moving vehicles or vehicles overturning. Many more are seriously injured in this way. The risks can be reduced if the use of vehicles and mobile plant is properly managed. Plan the site layout to reduce risks:

☐ provide safe site entry and exit points with adequate turning room and good visibility for vehicle drivers. Good visibility and lighting is especially important where vehicles must come close to pedestrians. Where necessary, provide a banksman or signaller;

☐ plan to keep pedestrians separate from vehicles by, for example, providing separate site entry and exit points and barriered footways. Make sure pedestrians have a good view of any vehicles at gates and other crossings;

☐ consider a one-way system and avoid the need for vehicles to reverse wherever possible;

☐ where reversing is necessary, consider fitting audible reversing alarms and visibility aids to vehicles;

☐ when necessary, make use of signallers to control high risk situations, for example, where vehicles are reversing or visibility is restricted. Ensure signallers are trained and wear high visibility clothing;

☐ train the drivers of all vehicles and make sure visiting drivers are informed about site transport rules;

☐ set out clear routes across the site avoiding sharp bends, blind corners (suitably placed mirrors aid visibility), narrow gaps, places with limited head room, overhead cables (see pages 87 to 88), steep gradients, adverse cambers, and shafts and excavations. Rollover protection and seat restraints should be fitted to vehicles where there is a risk that the vehicle may roll over. Provide extra lighting if the area is poorly lit;

☐ prepare the running surface of temporary roads. Where the site is muddy, skidding and bogging down may be a problem - consider using hardcore or other fill to overcome the problem and repair potholes;

☐ protect any temporary structures, such as scaffolds or falsework, which might be damaged and made unsafe if struck by a vehicle;

Here pedestrians are kept clear of vehicles. The roadway is well lit and a banksman is available to guide vehicles out of the site where visibility is restricted.

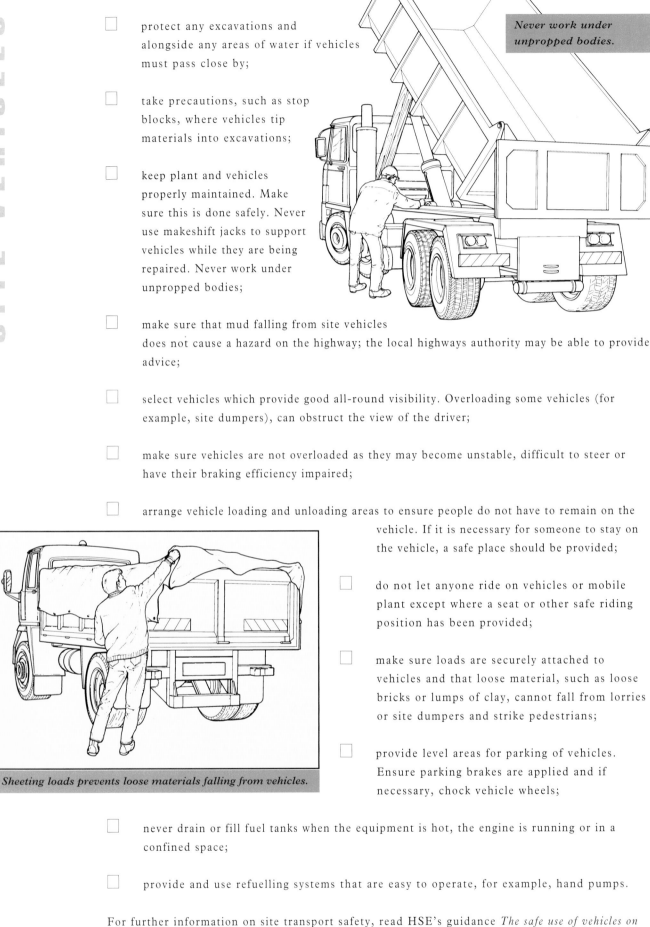

□ protect any excavations and alongside any areas of water if vehicles must pass close by;

□ take precautions, such as stop blocks, where vehicles tip materials into excavations;

□ keep plant and vehicles properly maintained. Make sure this is done safely. Never use makeshift jacks to support vehicles while they are being repaired. Never work under unpropped bodies;

Never work under unpropped bodies.

□ make sure that mud falling from site vehicles does not cause a hazard on the highway; the local highways authority may be able to provide advice;

□ select vehicles which provide good all-round visibility. Overloading some vehicles (for example, site dumpers), can obstruct the view of the driver;

□ make sure vehicles are not overloaded as they may become unstable, difficult to steer or have their braking efficiency impaired;

□ arrange vehicle loading and unloading areas to ensure people do not have to remain on the vehicle. If it is necessary for someone to stay on the vehicle, a safe place should be provided;

□ do not let anyone ride on vehicles or mobile plant except where a seat or other safe riding position has been provided;

□ make sure loads are securely attached to vehicles and that loose material, such as loose bricks or lumps of clay, cannot fall from lorries or site dumpers and strike pedestrians;

□ provide level areas for parking of vehicles. Ensure parking brakes are applied and if necessary, chock vehicle wheels;

Sheeting loads prevents loose materials falling from vehicles.

□ never drain or fill fuel tanks when the equipment is hot, the engine is running or in a confined space;

□ provide and use refuelling systems that are easy to operate, for example, hand pumps.

For further information on site transport safety, read HSE's guidance *The safe use of vehicles on construction sites*,[2] *Reversing vehicles*,[25] *Rider operated lift trucks - operator training*[26] and *Workplace transport safety - guidance for employers*.[27]

HEALTH HAZARDS

Hazardous substances and processes

Any hazardous substances that are going to be used, or processes which may produce hazardous materials, should be identified. The risks from work which might affect site workers or members of the public should then be assessed. Designers (see page 104) should eliminate hazardous materials from their designs. Where this is not possible, they should specify the least hazardous products which perform satisfactorily.

Contractors often have detailed knowledge of alternative, less hazardous materials. Designers and contractors can often help each other in identifying hazardous materials and processes and suggesting less hazardous alternatives.

If workers use or are exposed to hazardous substances as a result of their work, the Control of Substances Hazardous to Health Regulations (COSHH) 2002 make it a legal duty to assess the health risks involved and to prevent exposure or else adequately control it. There are separate regulations for asbestos and lead - the Control of Asbestos at Work Regulations 2002 (see pages 77 to 79) and the Control of Lead at Work Regulations 2002. HSE's booklet *Health risk management*[28] gives advice about how to identify and manage health risks.

Identification

People may be exposed to hazardous substances either because they handle or use them directly, (for example, solvents in glues and paints), or because the work itself results in the creation of a hazardous substance, (for example, scabbling concrete generates silica dust). Identify and assess both kinds of hazard.

If hazardous substances are going to be used, manufacturers and suppliers of such substances have a legal duty to provide information. Read the label on the container and/or the safety data sheet. Approach the manufacturer or supplier directly for more information if necessary.

Also, some hazardous substances may be on site before any work starts, for example, sewer gases (see Working in confined spaces, pages 59 to 61), or ground contaminants. Read *Protection of workers and the general public during the development of contaminated land.*[29] Assess these risks in the same way as for other hazardous substances. Information to help identify these risks may be available from the client, the design team or the principal contractor (see pages 103 to 106) or may be contained in the pre-construction stage health and safety plan (see pages 101 to 103).

Assessment

Look at the way people are exposed to the hazardous substance in the particular job that is about to be done. Decide whether it is likely to harm anyone's health. Harm could be caused by:

- **breathing in fumes, vapours, dust:** Does the manufacturer's information say that there is a risk from inhaling the substance? Are large amounts of the substance being used? Is the work being done in a way which results in heavy contamination of the air, for example, spray application? Is the work to be done in an area which is poorly ventilated, for example, a basement? Does the work generate a hazard, for example, hot cutting metal covered with lead causes lead fumes to be given off;

- **direct contact with skin or eyes:** Does the manufacturer's information say there is a risk from direct contact? How severe is it, for example, are strong acids or alkalis being used? Does the method of work make skin contact likely, for example, from splashes when pouring from one container to another or from the method of application;

- **swallowing or eating contaminated material:** Some dusty materials can contaminate the skin and hands. The contamination can then be passed to a person's mouth when they eat or smoke. This is a particular problem when handling lead and sanding lead-based paint. Make sure people do not smoke or eat without washing first (see pages 8 to 10 and page 76).

Once a full assessment has been completed and where the same work is being done in the same way under similar circumstances at a number of sites, the risk assessment does not have to be repeated before every job. Review the assessment from time to time, but every few years will probably be enough. However, look out for new products which could be safer substitutes.

If, however, there are many processes which result in different hazardous substances being used in a wide range of circumstances, a fresh assessment may be needed for each job or set of similar jobs. This will make sure the assessment is relevant to the job being done and the circumstances in which it is being carried out.

Remember to assess both immediate risks, for example, being overcome by fumes in a confined space, and longer term health risks. Materials like cement can cause dermatitis. Sensitising agents like isocyanates can make people using them have sudden reactions even though they may have used the substance many times before.

Prevention

If harm from the substance is likely, the first step to take is to try and avoid it completely by not using it at all. This will mean either:

☐ doing the job in a different way, for instance, instead of using acids or caustic soda to unblock a drain, use drain rods; or

☐ using a substitute substance, for example, instead of using spirit-based paints, use water-based ones which are generally less hazardous. However, always check one hazard is not simply being replaced by another.

Control

If the substance has to be used because there is no alternative, or because use of the least hazardous alternative still leads to significant risk, the next step is to try and control exposure. Some of the ways this could be done include the following:

☐ ensuring good ventilation in the working area by opening doors, windows and skylights. Mechanical ventilation equipment might be needed in some cases;

☐ using as little of the hazardous substances as possible - don't take more to the workplace than is needed;

☐ rather than spraying solvent-based materials, use a roller with a splash guard or apply by brush;

☐ transferring liquids with a pump or syphon (not one primed by mouth) rather than by hand. Keep containers closed except when transferring;

□ using cutting and grinding tools fitted with exhaust ventilation or water suppression to control dust; or

□ using blasting equipment fitted with exhaust ventilation or water suppression to control dust.

Personal protective equipment

If, and only if, exposure cannot be adequately controlled by any combination of the measures already mentioned, also provide personal protective equipment (PPE). This might take the form of:

□ respirators which can protect against dusts, vapours and gases. Make sure the respirator is of the correct type for the job; dust masks may not protect against vapours or vice versa. If the respirator has replaceable cartridges, make sure the correct type for the job is fitted, that it has not become exhausted or clogged and is still in date (many filters have a limited shelf life). It is essential that respirators fit well around the face. Make sure the user knows how to wear the equipment and check for a good face seal. Respirators do not usually seal well against a beard, so when users have a beard, other protection which does not rely on a good face seal is needed;

□ protective clothing, such as overalls, boots, gloves. Protection may be needed against corrosive substances;

□ eye protection, such as goggles or face visors. Protection of the eyes is important. If the protection needed is against corrosive splashes, visors can protect the whole face.

Select PPE with care. Choose good quality equipment which is CE-marked. Let the user of the equipment help choose it - they will be more willing to wear it. Explain to the user why the equipment has to be worn and the hazard(s) the equipment protects against. Users need to know how the equipment should be operated and what maintenance checks they should carry out. Supervise the user to make sure the equipment is being used properly. Regularly maintain the equipment and check it for damage. Store it in a dry, clean place and have replacement and spare equipment to hand.

In this chasing operation dust has been reduced by extraction at the tool. This ensures that people working in the area are not exposed to dust. The exposure of the operator is also much reduced, but a dust mask is still required for complete protection.

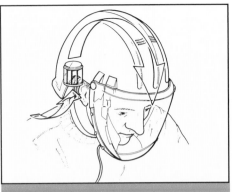

This helmet is fitted with a pump which provides a stream of filtered air to the inside of the visor. These helmets can provide protection for workers with beards as they do not rely on a good seal against the face. The stream of air across the face can also aid comfort in warm environments.

Make sure the PPE does not become a source of contamination by keeping the inside of dust masks and gloves clean. Store them in a clean box or cupboard - don't leave them lying around in the work area.

For further information on protective clothing and equipment, read *A short guide to the Personal Protective Equipment at Work Regulations 1992,*[30] and HSE's Construction Information Sheet *Personal Protective Equipment,* No 50.[31]

Personal hygiene

Substances can also be a hazard to health when they are transferred from workers' hands onto food, cigarettes etc and so taken into the body. This can be avoided by good personal hygiene, for example, by:

☐ washing hands and face before eating, drinking and smoking and before using the toilet;

☐ eating, drinking and smoking only away from the work area.

Make sure as few people as possible are exposed to the substances by excluding people not directly involved in the work from the contaminated area.

Make sure those at risk know the hazards. Provide good washing facilities and somewhere clean to eat meals. Good clean welfare facilities (see pages 8 to 12) can play an important part in protecting the health of everyone involved in the work.

COSHH is explained in *A step-by-step guide to COSHH assessment.*[32] Further details of COSHH requirements, including the text of the Regulations themselves, are given in the COSHH ACOP.[33]

Health surveillance

Sometimes workers' health can be protected by checking for early signs of illness. Such surveillance is a legal duty in a restricted range of cases for work involving some health risks such as asbestos. Surveillance may be appropriate in other cases: for example, for workers regularly engaged in blast-cleaning surfaces containing silica, or where workers are exposed to high levels of noise or hand-arm vibration, especially for long periods. For further information read *Health surveillance at work.*[34]

Asbestos

Asbestos-related diseases kill more people than any other single work-related cause. All types of asbestos can be dangerous if disturbed. The danger arises when asbestos fibres become airborne. They form a very fine dust which is often invisible. Breathing asbestos dust can cause serious damage to the lungs and cause cancer. There is no known cure for asbestos-related diseases.

The more asbestos dust inhaled, the greater the risk to health. Until recently it was thought that those dying from asbestos-related diseases were regularly exposed to large amounts of asbestos. It is now thought that repeated low exposures or occasional high exposures to asbestos can lead to asbestos induced cancers, though the exact scale of risk at lower levels of exposure is unknown. Therefore precautions should always be taken to prevent exposure, or where this is not practicable, to keep it to a minimum. Workers such as plumbers, electricians and heating engineers may not consider that they work with asbestos, but they might regularly drill, cut and handle materials containing asbestos and need to be protected.

The free HSE leaflet *A short guide to managing asbestos in premises*[35] contains essential, current guidance for workers and lists other useful publications on the subject. These include *Asbestos alert for building maintenance, repair and refurbishment workers*[36] and *Asbestos and man-made mineral fibres in buildings.*[37] Asbestos is a very durable fibre. It was widely used in materials where resistance to heat or chemical attack was important and to give strength to cement products such as insulation boards, corrugated roof sheets and cement guttering and pipework. Sprayed asbestos coatings have also been used to reduce noise.

For many jobs, building owners will already know where asbestos can be found in their buildings. In some cases they may even have labelled it to warn others who may come into contact with it. However, often the presence of asbestos will not be obvious. It is sensible to assume that any building constructed or refurbished before the 1980s will contain asbestos-based materials. No work should be carried out which is likely to expose employees to asbestos unless an adequate assessment of exposure has been made. This means that the building or area of the building where work is to be done should be checked to identify the location, type and condition of any asbestos which could be disturbed during the work.

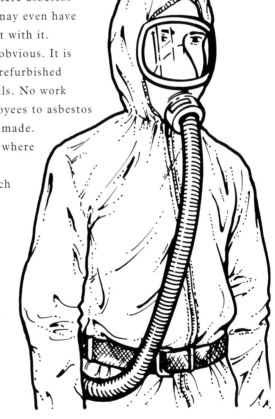

Some of the most common materials containing asbestos are:

- boiler and pipework coatings and laggings;

- sprayed coatings providing fire or acoustic insulation;

- insulation board;

Respiratory protection and disposable overalls are needed when working in higher levels of asbestos dust.

- cement-based boards, sheets and formed products;

- ceiling (and some floor) tiles;

- gaskets and paper products used for thermal and electrical insulation;

- some textured surface coatings.

Further information can be found in *Working with asbestos in buildings.*[38]

In general the softer the material the more easily it is damaged and the more likely it is to release fibres when disturbed or worked on. The greater the fibre release, the greater the risk to health it will generate and the higher the standard of precautions required when working with that material. Many of the softer materials, for example, boiler lagging, will be protected by a hard outer coating. If the protective outer coating could be inadvertently damaged during the work, take precautions either to protect it or to ensure that if it is damaged the subsequent release of asbestos will not create a risk. Work in which asbestos insulation, asbestos coating or asbestos insulating board is removed, repaired or disturbed will normally have to be carried out by a specialist contractor licensed under the Asbestos (Licensing) Regulations 1983 as amended.

If asbestos, or what is suspected to be asbestos, which was not identified during the initial assessment is discovered, stop work. Protect it from further damage until it has been decided how work can proceed in safety. If there is doubt about the presence of asbestos, seek the advice of a specialist analyst.

All work with asbestos and the precautions needed, is covered by the Control of Asbestos at Work Regulations 2002. The Regulations place a duty on an employer to prevent the exposure of employees to asbestos, or to reduce exposure to the lowest reasonably practicable level. So, if possible, a work method which avoids any disturbance of asbestos-containing materials should be chosen. If this is not possible, before carrying out any work which is liable to expose employees, or others, to asbestos, make an assessment of the likely exposure.

It is important to make this assessment even when exposure to asbestos is infrequent and only happens by chance, eg during building refurbishment or repair work such as gas fitting, plumbing or electrical work. The assessment will help in deciding what precautions need to be taken to protect people who may be affected by the work.

The Regulations are supported by two Approved Codes of Practice: *Work with asbestos which does not normally require a licence* (fourth edition)[39] and *Work with asbestos insulation, asbestos coating and asbestos insulating board* (fourth edition).[40]

Apart from a few limited exemptions, the Asbestos (Licensing) Regulations 1983 prohibit contractors working on asbestos insulation, asbestos coating or asbestos insulating board unless they have a licence issued by HSE. This is specialist work usually requiring the erection of enclosures around the work, filtered powered ventilation for the enclosure, high efficiency powered respirators and separate changing and showering facilities.

Essential points to remember when working with small quantities of hard asbestos-containing materials:

☐ there is no requirement for a licence to work on asbestos cement sheet, or with asbestos cement products like ducts and pipework, but the work must be done in compliance with the Control of Asbestos at Work Regulations 2002. An assessment of exposure is required. Avoid exposure to airborne dust and provide necessary protective equipment, including respirators. Only use respirators to control exposure after all other steps to reduce exposure have been taken. Further information can be found in the publication *Working with asbestos cement.*[41]

☐ apart from a few exemptions, work with asbestos coating, asbestos insulation, or asbestos insulating board requires a licence. Before starting work, check whether a licensed contractor should be doing it.

☐ where exposure is to low levels of fibre, for example, when removing small numbers of good condition ceiling tiles or drilling a few holes as part of plumbing or electrical work, disposable respirators may give adequate protection. For more extensive work involving breaking boarding or handling damaged materials, more precautions such as full-face respirators, disposable overalls and ventilated enclosures as required when working with lagging may be necessary;

☐ don't break asbestos board or sheeting; try to remove it as an undamaged piece. Where sheet has to be worked on, wet it first if possible. Handle the material carefully - don't drop materials onto the floor or ground. Pick up loose pieces immediately. If working outdoors, for example, taking down roof sheets, make sure vehicles don't run over sheets at ground level - this results in high dust levels;

☐ use hand tools - drilling and cutting sheet with power tools produces a lot of dust. Use the working methods and precautions described in the asbestos ACOP,[39] or other equally safe methods. Avoid blasting, sanding and grinding the material;

☐ if asbestos materials are removed, they must be disposed of safely. Board and sheet materials should usually be wrapped and sealed in polythene sheet and marked to indicate the presence of asbestos. Only specified tips accept asbestos-containing waste; check with the local waste disposal authority for details and see *Special Waste Regulations 1996: The controls on special waste: How they affect you.*[42]

Other relevant publications are: *Asbestos dust kills: Keep your mask on;*[43] *Selection of suitable RPE for work with asbestos;*[44] *Controlled asbestos stripping techniques for work requiring a licence;*[45] *Introduction to asbestos essentials;*[46] and *Asbestos essentials task manual*[47] - task guidance sheets for work of short duration work with asbestos containing materials aimed at the building maintenance and allied trades.

The Asbestos (Prohibitions) Regulations 1999 prohibit the import, supply and use of all types of asbestos and products containing them, apart from a few exemptions allowing the continued use of chrysotile (white) asbestos for a limited period (eg for aircraft components etc).

New products containing asbestos permitted as a derogation from the above regulations carry a warning label, as shown in Schedule 2 of the asbestos ACOP.[39]

Noise

Regular exposure to high noise levels causes deafness - the longer the exposure and the higher the noise level, the greater the degree of deafness which results.

The exposure of anyone to noise from work activities should be assessed and controlled. Where risk to hearing cannot be eliminated, provide hearing protection.

Check which work will involve noisy equipment. Assess how much the noise from this work is going to affect people working at the site and members of the public.

The manufacturers and suppliers of equipment have a legal duty to provide information on the noise equipment produces. This information should give a good idea if there is likely to be a noise problem. Go back to the manufacturer or supplier if the information is not clear. Where possible choose low noise tools and equipment.

Assessment

☐ Look at how equipment will actually be used on site. Can the person using the equipment talk to someone 2 m away without having to shout to be understood? If they have to shout, the noise from the equipment is probably loud enough to damage their hearing, so action will have to be taken.

☐ Get the noise levels assessed by someone with the skill and experience to measure noise and who can identify what needs to be done. In the meantime, offer workers ear defenders or plugs to wear.

☐ Tell all workers exposed above the action levels that there is a risk to their hearing, what is being done about it and what they are expected to do to minimise the risk.

Prevention

☐ Can the job be done in another way which does not involve using noisy equipment? If not, can a quieter item of equipment be used? When buying or hiring equipment, choose the quietest model. Try and carry out the noisy job well away from where other people are working. Move workers not involved out of the noisy area. Erect signs to keep people out of the noisy area.

Control

☐ Try and quieten the noise at source, for example, fit mufflers to breakers, drills etc. Keep the covers closed on compressors. Most modern compressors are designed to run with all covers closed, even in hot weather. Make sure the silencers on mobile plant are in good condition. Maintain equipment regularly to prevent noise from loose bearings and leaky compressed air hoses and joints.

☐ Noise levels can be reduced by making sure the exhausts of compressors, generators and other plant are directed away from work areas. Screens faced with sound-absorbent materials can be placed around plant. Material or spoil heaps can be used to act as noise barriers.

☐ If it is not possible to eliminate the noise source or reduce the noise, provide workers with ear plugs or defenders. Providing hearing protection is not a substitute for noise elimination and control at source.

Carefully select plugs and defenders, keep them in good condition and train workers in their use. Make sure that where defenders or plugs are needed they are actually used. Check that the hearing protection does not interfere with other safety equipment. For example, if ear defenders are difficult to wear with a hard hat, get defenders which fit onto the hat.

For further information read *Noise in construction*,[48] *Dust and noise in the construction process*[49] and *Noise at Work: Advice for employers*.[50]

Vibration

Many jobs in construction involve the use of hand-held power tools such as pneumatic breakers and disc grinders. The vibration from such equipment can affect the fingers, hands and arms and, in the long term, do permanent damage. Parts of the fingers go white and numb and there is a loss of touch.

If anyone uses hand-held power tools, they should identify, assess and prevent or control the risk from vibration.

The manufacturer or supplier's information should indicate if there is a vibration problem. Go back to the manufacturer or supplier if the information is not clear. Where possible choose low vibration tools.

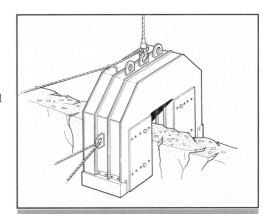

Crushers can be used instead of hand-held breakers. This reduces exposure to vibration, noise and dust; it may also be quicker and cheaper.

Assessment

The information from the manufacturer or supplier, the amount of time the tools are used and discussions with the people using the tools should reveal the tools most likely to present a risk.

Make sure workers using vibrating tools know about the risks and what they need to do to minimise them. Further information for workers is provided by HSE's guidance *Hand-arm vibration syndrome: Pocket card for employees*.[51]

Prevention

Can the job be done in another way which does not involve using hand-held power tools (for example, by using a hydraulic breaker to break a concrete beam rather than spending long periods using hand-held breakers)?

Control

Maintain equipment so that it is properly balanced, has no loose or worn out parts and blades/cutters are sharp etc. Use the power tool and attachment which will do the job properly in the shortest time.

To protect against vibration, workers should keep their hands warm to get a good flow of blood into the fingers by:

• wearing gloves;

• having hot food or drinks;

• massaging the fingers;

•   not smoking (as this can cause narrowing of the blood vessels).

For further information on vibration, see HSE's guidance *Hand-arm vibration*[52] and *Power tools: How to reduce vibration health risks.*[53]

PROTECTIVE EQUIPMENT

Advice about respirators and other equipment to protect against hazardous substances such as dusts, gases and vapours and against noise and vibration can be found in the section on hazardous substances (see pages 73 to 81). This section gives advice about other equipment which may be required to protect against injury.

On almost all sites there is a risk of injury from falling materials and a risk of foot injury. Minimise these risks by providing suitable barriers and toe boards or other equipment at the edge of work platforms to prevent materials from falling. Keep the site tidy and maintain clear walkways. Deal with the remaining risks by providing suitable hard hats and footwear.

Hard hats

The Construction (Head Protection) Regulations 1989 make specific requirements about hard hats - see HSE's publication[54] for detailed guidance on the Regulations. Hard hats are required where anybody might be struck by falling materials or where people might hit their heads.

These are just some of the hazards to consider:

•   loose material being kicked into an excavation;

•   material falling from a scaffold platform;

•   material falling off a load being lifted by a crane or goods hoist or carried on a site dumper or truck;

•   a scaffolder dropping a fitting while erecting or dismantling a scaffold.

Decide on which areas of the site hats have to be worn. Tell everyone in the area; if necessary, make site rules.

Provide employees with hard hats. Make sure hats are worn and worn correctly. A wide range of hats is available. Let employees try a few and decide which is most suitable for the job and for them. Some hats have extra features including a sweat band for the forehead and a soft, or webbing, harness. Although these hats are slightly more expensive, they are much more comfortable and therefore more likely to be worn.

Footwear

Is there a risk of injury from either:

•   materials being dropped on workers' feet; or

•   nails, or other sharp objects, penetrating the sole?

If so, boots with toe caps and sole-plates may be needed.

Where it is likely that employees will be working in water or wet concrete, wellington boots should be provided.

Boots with toe caps and sole-plates may be needed.

Goggles and safety spectacles

These are required to protect against:

- flying objects, for example, when using a nail gun. To provide adequate protection goggles should be shatter-proof - check the manufacturer's specification;

- sparks, for example, when disc-cutting;

- ultraviolet radiation from welding; specialist goggles or shields are required;

- chemical splashes.

Outdoor clothing

Where employees regularly work outdoors and they cannot be sheltered from the weather, clothing which is wind and waterproof will be needed. There should be facilities for storing clothing not worn on site and protective clothing as well as for drying wet clothing. (See welfare section, pages 8 to 12.)

High visibility clothing

Many accidents happen when people in hazardous positions cannot be seen. It is important to plan work to avoid placing people in these positions. Where this is not possible, provide high visibility clothing.

It is essential that this clothing be kept clean if it is to be effective. Badly soiled garments should be replaced.

High visibility clothing will be needed wherever workers:

- could be run down by vehicles, for example, signallers assisting in vehicles being manoeuvred and anyone engaged in roadworks;
- need to be seen by others to allow them to work safely, for example, signallers assisting in lifting operations need to be clearly visible to the crane driver.

Gloves

Suitable gloves can protect against dusts (such as cement), wet concrete and solvents which can cause dermatitis. They can also protect against cuts and splinters when handling bricks, steel and wood.

ELECTRICITY

Electrical equipment is used on virtually every site. Everyone is familiar with it, but not all seem to remember that electricity can kill. Electrical systems and equipment must be properly selected, installed, used and maintained.

It is essential that the electricity power supply requirements are established before any work takes place. Arrangements for the electricity supply should be completed with the local electricity supplier and the supply system installed. Guidance on requirements for low voltage ie 400 and/or 230 volt a.c systems can be found in BS 7671.[55]

Electrical equipment used on building sites, particularly power tools and other portable equipment and their leads, faces harsh conditions and rough use. It is likely to be damaged and becomes dangerous. Modern double insulated tools are well protected, but their leads are still vulnerable to damage and should be regularly checked.

Where possible, eliminate risks. Cordless tools or tools which operate from a 110V supply system which is centre-tapped to earth so that the maximum voltage to earth should not exceed 55V, will effectively eliminate the risk of death and greatly reduce injury in the event of an electrical accident. For other purposes such as lighting, particularly in confined and wet locations, still lower voltages can be used and are even safer.

If mains voltage has to be used, the risk of injury is high if equipment, tools, leads etc are damaged, or there is a fault. Residual current devices (RCDs or trip devices as they are sometimes called) with a rated tripping current not greater than 30 mA with no time delay will be needed to ensure that the current is promptly cut off if contact is made with any live part.

RCDs must be installed and treated with great care if they are to save life in an accident. They have to be kept free of moisture and dirt and protected against vibration and mechanical damage. They need to be properly installed and enclosed, including sealing of all cable entries. They should be checked daily by operating the test button. If mains voltage is to be used, make sure that tools can only be connected to sockets protected by RCDs. By installing it at the start of the work, immediate protection can be provided. Even so, RCDs cannot give the assurance of safety that cordless equipment or a reduced low voltage (such as 110V) system provides.

Mains equipment is more appropriate to dry indoor sites where damage from heavy or sharp materials is unlikely. Where mains leads to sockets may be damaged they should be:

☐ positioned where they are least likely to be damaged, for example, run cables at ceiling height; or

☐ protected inside impact resistant conduit.

Alternatively, special abrasion resistant or armoured flexible leads can be used.

Electrical systems should be regularly checked and maintained. Everyone using electrical equipment should know what to look out for. A visual inspection can detect about 95% of faults or damage. Before any 230V hand tool, lead or RCD is used, check that:

☐ no bare wires are visible;

☐ the cable covering is not damaged and is free from cuts and abrasions (apart from light scuffing);

☐ the plug is in good condition, for example, the casing is not cracked, the pins are not bent and the key way is not blocked with loose material;

☐ there are no taped or other non-standard joints in the cable;

☐ the outer covering (sheath) of the cable is gripped where it enters the plug or the equipment. The coloured insulation of the internal wires should not be visible;

☐ the outer case of the equipment is not damaged or loose and all screws are in place;

☐ there are no overheating or burn marks on the plug, cable or the equipment;

☐ RCDs are working effectively, by pressing the 'test' button every day.

Workers should be instructed to report any of these faults immediately and stop using the tool or cable as soon as any damage is seen. Managers should also arrange for a formal visual inspection of 230V portable equipment on a weekly basis.

Damaged equipment should be taken out of service as soon as the damage is noticed. Do not carry out makeshift repairs.

Some faults, such as the loss of earth continuity due to wires breaking or coming loose within the equipment, the breakdown of insulation and internal contamination (for example, dust containing metal particles may cause shorting if it gets inside the tool), will not be spotted by visual inspections. To identify these problems, a programme of testing and inspection is necessary. This testing and inspection should be carried out by someone trained to do this. As well as testing as part of the planned maintenance programme, combined inspection and testing should also be carried out:

• if there is reason to suspect the equipment may be faulty, damaged or contaminated, but this cannot be confirmed by visual inspection; and

• after any repair, modification or similar work to the equipment, which could have affected its electrical safety.

Similar checks to those recommended for 230V hand tools are appropriate for other site electrical equipment. Suggestions for inspections and test frequencies are set out in the table on page 86.

With lighting systems, provide protection for cabling in the same way as for tools. Protect bulbs against breakage. If breakage does occur the exposed filaments may present a hazard. Make sure there is a system for checking bulbs to maintain electrical safety and also to keep the site well lit.

Tools and equipment should be suitable for site conditions. DIY tools and domestic plugs and cables are not designed to stand up to everyday construction work. Also observe other restrictions on use imposed by manufacturers.

EQUIPMENT/ APPLICATION	VOLTAGE	USER CHECK	FORMAL VISUAL INSPECTION	COMBINED INSPECTION AND TEST
Battery-operated power tools and torches	Less than 25 volts	NO	NO	NO
25V Portable hand lamps (confined or damp situations)	25 volt Secondary winding from transformer	NO	NO	NO
50V Portable hand lamps	Secondary winding centre tapped to earth (25 volt)	NO	NO	Yearly
110V Portable and hand-held tools, extension leads, site lighting, moveable wiring systems and associated switchgear	Secondary winding centre tapped to earth (55 volt)	Weekly	Monthly	Before first use on site and then 3 monthly
230V Portable and hand-held tools, extension leads and portable floodlighting	230 volt mains supply through 30 mA RCD	Daily/ every shift	Weekly	Before first use on site and then monthly
230V Equipment such as lifts, hoists and fixed floodlighting	230V Supply fuses or MCBs	Weekly	Monthly	Before first use on site and then 3 monthly
RCD's Portable		Daily/ every shift	Weekly	*Before first use on site and then monthly
RCDs Fixed		Daily/ every shift	Weekly	*Before first use on site and then 3 monthly
Equipment in site offices	230 volt Office equipment	Monthly	6 Monthly	Before first use on site and then yearly

Note: RCDs need a different range of tests to other portable equipment, and equipment designed to carry out appropriate tests on RCDs will need to be used.

If work is to be done in areas where there is a risk of flammable vapours such as in a petro-chemical works, it may be necessary to select specially designed electrical equipment to prevent it acting as a source of ignition, due to sparks and overheating. Precautions should be covered in the health and safety plan for the project and the operator of the premises should be able to provide advice. Specialist advice may also be needed.

For further information, see *Maintaining portable and transportable electrical equipment*[56] and *Memorandum of guidance on the Electricity at Work Regulations 1989.*[57]

Further information on controlling electrical risks can be found in *Electrical safety on construction sites.*[58] More information on risks from buried cables can be found on pages 57 to 58.

Overhead power lines

Contact with overhead electric lines is a regular cause of death and injury. Any work near electric distribution cables or railway power lines must be carefully planned to avoid accidental contact.

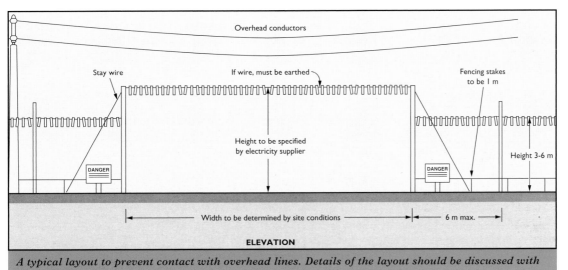

A typical layout to prevent contact with overhead lines. Details of the layout should be discussed with the line owner.

The most common operations leading to contact with overhead lines are:

• handling long scaffold tubes;

• handling long metal roof sheets;

• handling long ladders;

• operating cranes and other lifting plant;

• raising the body or inclined container of tipper lorries; and

• using MEWPs.

Where possible all work likely to lead to contact with the overhead line should be done in an area well clear of the line itself.

In some cases it may be possible to alter the work to eliminate the risk, for example, by reducing the length of scaffold tubes, ladders or roof sheets to ensure that the line cannot be contacted accidentally.

As a general rule no vehicles, plant or equipment should be brought closer than:

- 15 m of overhead lines suspended from steel towers; or

- 9 m of overhead lines supported on wooden poles.

In cases where closer approach is likely, it is necessary either to have the lines made dead or to erect barriers to prevent approach to them. Where work is to take place close to overhead lines, detailed precautions should be discussed with the owner of the lines (any work next to any railway where the work is likely to encroach onto railway land should, in any case, be discussed with the railway operator before work begins).

For more information, read *Avoidance of danger from overhead electric powerlines.* [59]

WORK AFFECTING THE PUBLIC

It is not only workers who are at risk from construction work. Members of the public are killed and seriously injured each year. The dead and injured include children.

Accidents often happen when people are walking near a building being built, refurbished or demolished, or walking near work in the street. Remember, when working in public areas, the work needs to be planned and executed to take account of the needs of children, people with prams, the elderly and those with disabilities.

Main points to consider

☐ **Falling materials:** Protect passers-by with brickguards and/or netting on scaffolding, but remember, most netting will only retain light material. Fans and/or covered walkways may also be needed where the risk is particularly high. Use plastic sheeting on scaffolds to retain dust, drips and splashes which may occur when cleaning building facades. Make sure the sheets do not make the scaffold unstable.

When using gin wheels or power driven hoists, select a safe place where members of the public are not at risk. Use hooks with safety catches when lifting (see page 66). Use debris chutes when removing debris into a skip; cover over the skip to stop flying debris and cut down dust.

Remove loose materials and debris from scaffold platforms. Do not stack materials on scaffolds unless it is needed and then not above the level of the toe board unless brickguards or another way of retaining material has been provided.

Remove or tie down loose materials and scaffold boards if high winds are possible. Make sure site hoardings will stand up to high winds.

☐ **Dusty and hot work:** Fence off hot work such as welding or the use of disc cutters to contain dust and sparks. Fence off bitumen and similar boilers which have to be sited in a public space.

☐ **Site visitors:** Make sure site visitors report to the person in charge of the site and know where to go - notices at the site entrance may be required. A waiting area may be needed. Visitors should not be allowed to wander around the site alone. A booking-in system may be needed on larger sites.

When housing estates are being built or properties are being refurbished, people not involved in the work who are also unfamiliar with construction site hazards may well want to look around the site. Make sure they are accompanied at all times and given any necessary protective equipment such as helmets or boots. Programme operations so that work is not in progress on the parts of the site the public visit regularly. Arrange and sign access routes across the site to keep visitors away from site hazards.

Keeping the public out: In most cases a 2 m perimeter fence will need to be put up and maintained. If alterations are needed or safeguards have to be taken down, make sure they are put back when the job is finished, before leaving the site for meal breaks, and at the end of the day. Lock the site gates and any other doors and windows at night.

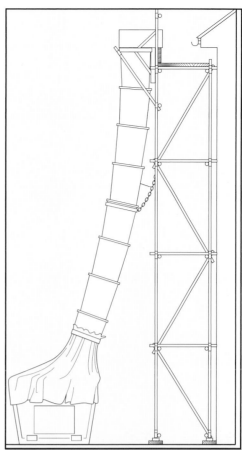

Position skips to collect material from chutes. Cover the skip to retain dust and flying materials. If a skip is not in place, cover the entry to the chute to prevent it being used. Prevent children using the chute as a slide.

If work is being done in occupied premises, clear responsibilities for maintaining precautions and keeping those not involved in the work away need to be agreed with the occupier of the building.

If the site is near a school or on, or near a housing estate, it may be helpful to contact the head teacher and residents' association, etc to seek their help to discourage children from trespassing.

Many children see construction sites as adventure playgrounds. Even though they may be entering the site without authority or may be trespassing, they should still be protected from site dangers; many will be too young to appreciate the risks they are running.

Take the following steps to reduce the chance of children injuring themselves if they do get onto the site. At the end of the working day:

•   barrier off or cover over excavations, pits etc;

•   isolate and immobilise vehicles and plant; if possible lock them in a compound;

•   store building materials, such as pipes, manhole rings, cement bags etc so that they cannot topple or roll over;

- remove access ladders from excavations and scaffolds; and

- lock away hazardous substances.

Security measures may also be needed. These can often strengthen safety measures.

☐ **Work in the roadway or footway:** When working on the footpath or roadway, there could be a hazard to pedestrians and traffic. Road traffic may also present a hazard to the people on site. The Code of Practice, *Safety at street works and road works*[60] relating to the New Roads and Street Works Act 1991, gives advice about traffic signing, the protection of work areas and pedestrian diversions.

When planning work in streets or similar areas consider:

- signs for traffic and pedestrians;

- temporary traffic controls;

- cones or other barriers to mark the safety zone;

- barriers to protect the public. Barriers around street works perform two functions. First, they alert the public to the presence of such work and help to direct them away from the site. Secondly, if members of the public do approach the site, the barriers should be of sufficient strength and stability to prevent them being injured if they fall;

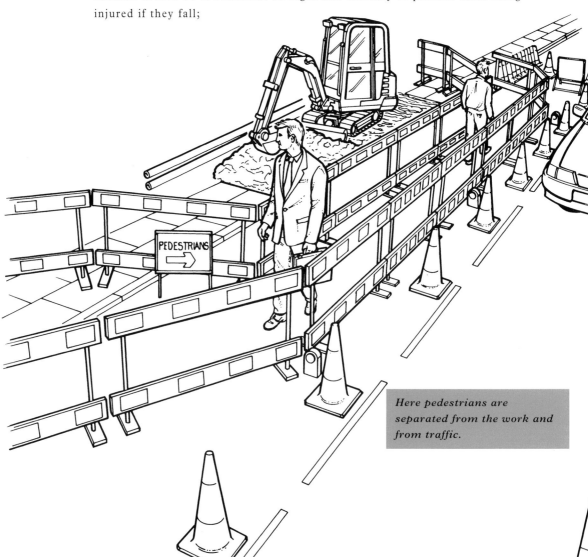

Here pedestrians are separated from the work and from traffic.

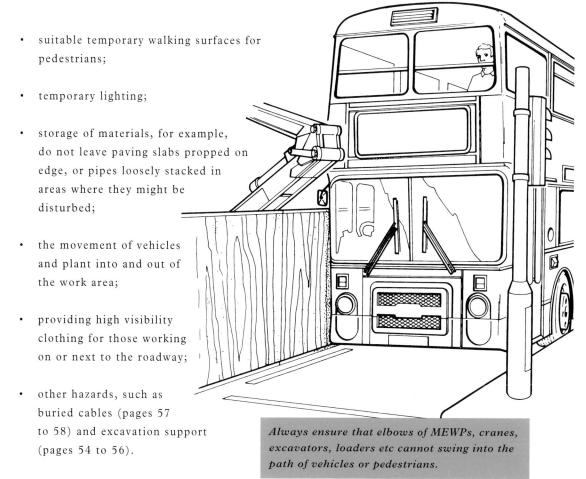

- suitable temporary walking surfaces for pedestrians;

- temporary lighting;

- storage of materials, for example, do not leave paving slabs propped on edge, or pipes loosely stacked in areas where they might be disturbed;

- the movement of vehicles and plant into and out of the work area;

- providing high visibility clothing for those working on or next to the roadway;

- other hazards, such as buried cables (pages 57 to 58) and excavation support (pages 54 to 56).

Always ensure that elbows of MEWPs, cranes, excavators, loaders etc cannot swing into the path of vehicles or pedestrians.

Tripping hazards: Fence excavations in the footpath or roadway. Store work materials out of the path of pedestrians and road users. Keep pavements free of tripping hazards. Make good any damage (temporarily if necessary) as soon as possible. Watch out for trailing cables.

Extra lighting might be needed at night if there is insufficient street lighting. On some occasions the pavement will have to be closed to protect the public, for example, during pavement work, demolition work, facade cleaning, raising hot asphalt, scaffold erection or dismantling. The area may need to be barriered off and a safe alternative route provided for pedestrians. Get in touch with the Highways Authority for advice.

For further information on preventing accidents to children on construction sites and other aspects of site security, see *Protecting the public - your next move.*[5]

3: HEALTH AND SAFETY MANAGEMENT AND THE LAW

All work activities are covered by health and safety law. The law which is most relevant to construction health and safety is set out here.

THE HEALTH AND SAFETY AT WORK ETC ACT 1974

This Act applies to all work activities. It requires employers to ensure so far as reasonably practicable the health and safety of their employees, other people at work and members of the public who may be affected by their work.

Employers should have a health and safety policy. If they employ five or more people, the policy should be in writing. Use the advice in this book to draw up a policy. Keep the policy clear and simple. Make sure everybody in the firm knows about and understands the health and safety systems which have been developed.

The self-employed should ensure so far as reasonably practicable their own health and safety and make sure that their work does not put other workers, or members of the public, at risk.

Employees have to co-operate with their employer on health and safety matters and not do anything that puts them or others at risk (see page 107). Employees should be trained and clearly instructed in their duties.

HSC has published guidance on the Act: *Health and safety regulation: A short guide.*[61]

THE MANAGEMENT OF HEALTH AND SAFETY AT WORK REGULATIONS 1999

The Management of Health and Safety at Work Regulations (MHSW Regulations) 1999 apply to everyone at work, regardless of what work it is. They require employers to plan, control, organise, monitor and review their work.

To do this they should:

☐ assess the risks associated with work to identify the control measures necessary to reduce these risks (see pages 94 to 95);

☐ have access to competent health and safety advice;

☐   provide health and safety information and training to employees;

☐   have arrangements to deal with serious and imminent danger;

☐   co-operate in health and safety matters with others who share the workplace.

Risk assessment

Employers and the self-employed must identify the hazards involved with their work, assess the likelihood of any harm arising and decide on adequate precautions. This process is called risk assessment and is central to all planning for health and safety.

How is a risk assessment carried out?

A risk assessment can be done in five steps:

STEP 1: Looking for the hazards. Consider the job, how it will be done, where it is done and what equipment, materials and chemicals are used. The process is like that described for the Control of Substances Hazardous to Health Regulations 1999 (COSHH - see pages 73 to 75) and noise (see page 80) assessments.

What are the hazards which could cause harm?

Here are some examples which are regular causes of serious and fatal accidents or ill health:

*   falling from an open edge or through a fragile material;

*   being struck by site vehicles;

*   collapse of an excavation or part of a structure;

*   work with materials (for example, lead, asbestos or solvents) which could be a health problem;

*   dust from cutting, grinding, drilling or scabbling.

The most common construction hazards are identified in Sections 1 and 2.

STEP 2: Decide who might be harmed and how. Think about employees, the self-employed, employees of other companies working on the job, site visitors and members of the public who may be in the area or outside the site.

Safe working often depends on co-operation between firms. Consider how they need to be taken into account in the assessment. Identify problems the work may cause for others at the site, or problems they may cause for those doing the work and agree necessary precautions. Tell the principal contractor or whoever is controlling the site what has been agreed.

STEP 3: Evaluate the risks and decide on action. This means asking if somebody is likely to be harmed. Where there is a risk of harm consider:

First: Can the hazard be removed completely? Could the job be done in another way or by using a different, less hazardous, material? If it can, change the job or process to eliminate the risk.

Example

A house builder's employees were lifting roof trusses into place from the ground by hand. The trusses were heavy and there was a risk that:

■ the workers would suffer strain injuries; and

■ the trusses would be dropped and injure someone.

By using a crane these risks were significantly reduced (cranes present their own risks!).

Second: If the risk cannot be eliminated, can it be controlled? Applying the advice and guidance given in Section 2 will help here. For example, while it may be necessary to apply a solvent-based material, the exposure of workers to hazardous vapours may be reduced by applying it by brush or roller rather than by spraying. If the precautions described in Section 2 have not been taken, is there an equivalent or better standard of protection? If not, more needs to be done.

Third: Can protective measures be taken which will protect the whole workforce? For example, to prevent falls, guard rails at edges provide safety for everyone in the area. Secured harnesses only provide safety for those wearing them and then only after a fall. They are a second best option.

STEP 4: Record the findings. Employers with five or more employees should record the significant findings of their assessment as an aid to controlling hazards and risks. Employers should pass on information about significant risks and the steps they have taken to control the risks, even when they employ less than five people.

STEP 5: Review the findings. Reviews are important. They take account of unusual conditions on some sites and changes in the way the job is done. Reviews allow lessons learned from experience to be taken into account. A new assessment is not always needed for every job, but if there are major changes a new assessment will be needed. In other cases only the principal contractor will be in a position to do a full assessment. For example, it may be the potential interaction of two or more contractors that leads to increased risk. In such cases the principal contractor (see page 105) should take the lead.

A form on which the risk assessment can be recorded is provided in *Five steps to risk assessment.*[62] Further advice on how risk assessment provisions in different regulations are linked together and what they mean can be found in *A guide to risk assessment requirements.*[63]

Method statements

Method statements are not required by law, but they have proved to be an effective and practical management tool. They can take account of risks identified by the risk assessment and communicate the safe system of work to those undertaking it, especially for higher risk complex or unusual work (for example, steel and formwork erection, demolition or the use of hazardous substances). A method statement draws together the information compiled about the various hazards and the ways in which they are to be controlled for any particular job.

A method statement takes into account the conclusions of assessments made under the MHSW Regulations as well as any assessments required by the Control of Substances Hazardous to Health Regulations 2002, the Manual Handling Operations Regulations 1992 etc. It also takes account of the company's health and safety organisation and training procedures and may include arrangements to deal with serious or imminent danger.

The method statement sets out how a job or process will be carried out, including all the control measures. This will allow the job to be properly planned and resourced with the appropriate health and safety resources needed for it. It can also provide information for other contractors working at the site about any effects the work will have on them and help the principal contractor to develop an overall health and safety plan for the construction phase of a project (see pages 101-103).

If a similar operation is repeated, the statement will be similar from job to job. However, if circumstances change markedly, for example, with demolition, the statement may need to be revised for each job.

The method statement is an effective way of providing information to employees about how the work is expected to be done and the precautions that should be taken. The most effective health and safety method statements often have a number of diagrams to make it clear how work should be carried out. Checking that the working methods set out in the statement are actually put into practice on site can also be a useful monitoring tool.

When reviewing the risk assessments, use the information from monitoring previous jobs and accident records and investigations (see page 97). It will help to decide if adequate precautions are being applied.

Health and safety training and advice

Somebody will need to be responsible for the firm's health and safety functions. This will make sure health and safety is not missed or ignored and allows an expertise to be built up in the firm. The person responsible may need extra training in health and safety to meet this responsibility properly. If employers don't do the job themselves, whoever is appointed must have the employers' full backing.

As with all training, whether for managers or site workers, there is a need to identify:

•   what they know already;

•   what the people need to know and what skills they need;

•   how best to provide the extra knowledge and skills they need.

Employers can then decide whether to provide the training in-house, use an external training course, or a consultant.

Extra advice can be found in a number of sources, many of which will be listed in local telephone directories. Keep the company up-to-date with developments in health and safety, such as new legal requirements. Subscribing to a health and safety journal may be a good way to do this.

If there isn't adequate expertise in the company, get help from the following:

- the Construction Industry Training Board (CITB);

- employers and trade organisations such as the Building Employers Confederation (BEC) and the Federation of Master Builders (FMB);

- Training and Enterprise Councils and Local Enterprise Companies;

- local health and safety groups;

- insurance companies;

- suppliers - they must provide instructions on using machines, tools, chemicals etc and product data sheets - also containers often have helpful labels;

- safety magazines - they have useful articles and advertise safety products and services;

- the British Safety Council (BSC), the Royal Society for the Prevention of Accidents (RoSPA), the Institution of Occupational Safety and Health (IOSH) and many other independent companies and consultants run training courses - look in the telephone directory;

- HSC publishes a newsletter[64] about new HSE publications, changes in the law and similar items of interest and there is also a twice yearly newsletter for the construction industry, *Site Safe News*.[65] If you wish to receive copies the addresses to contact are on page 115.

- the HSE website: www.hse.gov.uk;

HSE's booklet *Need help on health and safety?*[66] gives further advice.

Workers must be trained in safe working practices. Employees cannot be relied upon to pick up safety training on the job from their work-mates - they might simply be learning someone else's bad habits. Employers need to be sure of the abilities of their employees before setting them to work and to provide necessary training where it is required.

Foremen and supervisors play an important role in ensuring how work is done. They control the way in which work is carried out on site. This means they can and should ensure that work is safe. They also have an important role in passing on training and information to workers on site such as with toolbox talks. However, they cannot do this properly unless they are trained in safe and healthy working practices (see Section 2).

Monitoring health and safety

With any business activity checks need to be made from time to time to make sure that what should be happening is actually being carried out in practice; this includes health and safety. Make sure that everyone is fulfilling their duties. If a supervisor is nominated or a safety adviser is employed to visit sites and review safety, do they report problems to the site manager and to the employer? Are matters put right? Do the same problems keep recurring? If there are problems, find out why. Keeping a record of accidents, illnesses and treatments given by first aiders will help to identify trends. New instructions may need to be issued or extra training provided.

Act before there is an accident or someone's health is damaged. If an accident happens, find out what happened and why. Minor accidents and 'near misses' can give an early warning of more serious problems. Consider whether the accident would have happened if the work had been better planned or managed or employees had been better trained. Could site or company rules have been clearer or could plant and equipment have been better maintained? Don't just put the blame on human error or other people without thinking why the error was made.

THE CONSTRUCTION (HEALTH, SAFETY AND WELFARE) REGULATIONS 1996

Who has duties under the Regulations?

The main dutyholders under these Regulations are employers, the self-employed and those who control the way in which construction work is carried out. Employees too have duties to carry out their own work in a safe way. Also, anyone doing construction work has a duty to report any health or safety defects to those in control and to co-operate with others on matters of health and safety.

What do the Regulations cover?

The Regulations cover a wide range of health and safety problems, including:

- the provision of working platforms;

- the prevention of falls;

- the support of excavations;

- provisions for higher risk trades such as roofing, demolition and structural erection.

- emergency and fire procedures; and

- transport routes.

Much of the advice in Sections 1 and 2 of this book is relevant to these Regulations.

THE CONSTRUCTION (HEAD PROTECTION) REGULATIONS 1989

For details of when hard hats are required and details of further guidance, see page 82.

THE PROVISION AND USE OF WORK EQUIPMENT REGULATIONS 1998

These regulations cover all types of work equipment and deal with such issues as dangerous parts of machinery, roll over protections, visibility, and inspection. For further information read the Approved Code of Practice and guidance *Safe use of work equipment.*[67]

THE LIFTING OPERATIONS AND LIFTING EQUIPMENT REGULATIONS 1998

These regulations cover the operation of all lifting equipment including those which lift people. General advice on compliance can be found in the section entitled Moving, lifting and handling loads. Information on the regulations can be found in the Approved Code of Practice and guidance *Safe use of lifting equipment.*[68]

THE CONSTRUCTION (DESIGN AND MANAGEMENT) REGULATIONS 1994

The Construction (Design and Management) Regulations 1994 (CDM) require that health and safety is taken into account and managed throughout all stages of a project, from conception, design and planning through to site work and subsequent maintenance and repair of the structure.

Who does CDM affect?

CDM affects everyone who takes part in the construction process - the client, the designers and contractors. The Regulations introduce two new roles - the planning supervisor and the principal contractor. The Regulations also introduce the health and safety plan and the health and safety file. Make sure health and safety policies and procedures take account of the requirements of the CDM Regulations.

What does CDM require?

CDM requires that everyone who can contribute to improving site health and safety plays their part. What each dutyholder can do will vary from project to project. The efforts everyone makes should be proportional to the health and safety risks associated with the work and the difficulty of managing those risks. This means that for small, easily managed low risk projects very little is required. If the project is complex and the risks are high, much more effort is needed.

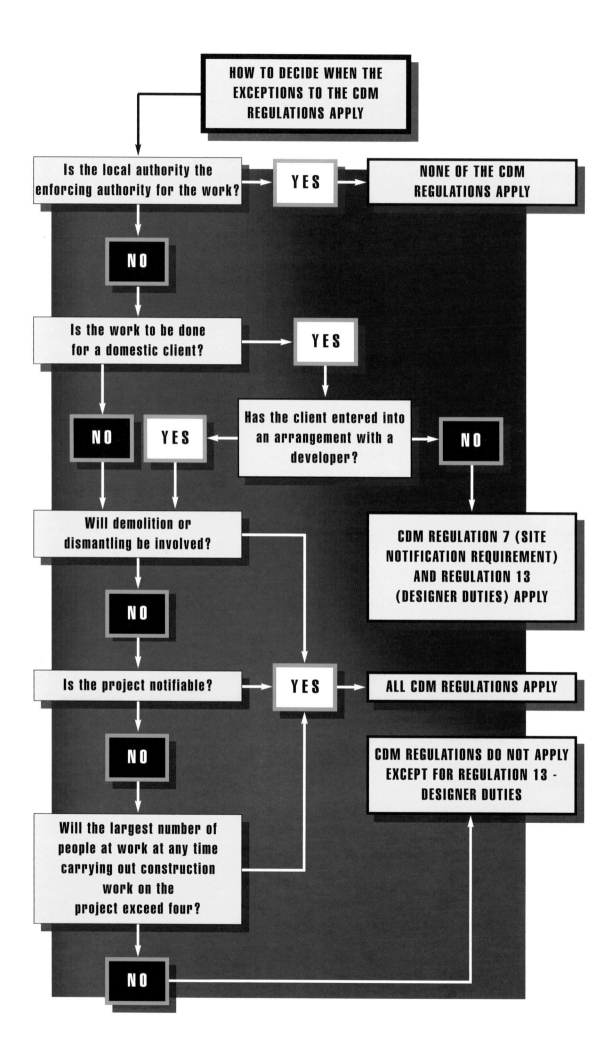

When does CDM apply?

The Regulations apply to most common building, civil engineering and engineering construction work. They do not apply to construction work where the local authority is the enforcing authority for health and safety purposes. This means that where work is not notifiable (see page 20) and is either:

- carried out inside offices, shops and similar premises where the construction work is done without interrupting the normal activities in the premises and without separating the construction activities from the other activities; or

- the maintenance or removal of insulation on pipes, boilers or other parts of heating or water systems;

it is not subject to the CDM Regulations.

Apart from this exception, the CDM Regulations apply to all design work carried out for construction purposes (including demolition and dismantling).

As far as contractors are concerned, the CDM Regulations apply to all demolition and dismantling work. They also apply to other construction work unless:

- the work will last 30 days or less and involve less than five people on site at any one time; or

- the work is being done for a domestic client (that is someone who lives, or will live, in the premises where the work is being done). In this case only the duties to notify HSE and those placed on designers apply (see page 104). However, in some instances domestic clients may enter into an arrangement with a developer who carries on a trade, business or other activity. For example, a developer may sell domestic premises before the project is complete. The domestic client then owns the incomplete property, but the developer still arranges for the construction work to be carried out. In this case the CDM requirements apply to the developer.

What is the health and safety plan?

The health and safety plan develops with the project and has at least two clear phases (the first is associated with design and planning of the project before tendering or contractor selection, the second is associated with the construction phase). The planning supervisor is responsible for seeing that the plan is started. The purpose of the plan is to ensure information relevant to health and safety is passed on to those who need it. The pre-construction stage health and safety plan may include:

☐ a general description of the work and details of project timescales;

☐ details of health and safety risks as far as they are known, including information provided by designers about particular project risks they were unable to eliminate and assumptions in broad terms they have made about precautions which will be taken;

☐ information required by possible principal contractors to allow them to identify the health and safety competences and resources they will need for the project;

☐ information on which to base a construction phase health and safety plan.

The pre-construction stage health and safety plan needs to be available to possible principal contractors at the start of selection or tendering procedures. It informs them of the health, safety and welfare matters they need to take into account when planning for site work. Often the necessary information will already be contained within existing documents (for example, preliminary documents and design drawings). In these cases the plan can simply be an index to where the necessary information within the other documents can be found. Where this is not the case, a separate plan containing the additional material will be required.

The plan only needs to contain information which is specific to the project and is necessary to assist the development of safe systems of work. The plan does not need to repeat information which a competent contractor would already know. Including unnecessary or irrelevant material can make essential information more difficult to identify and reduce the effectiveness of the plan as a way of passing on information.

For the construction phase the principal contractor develops the health and safety plan so that it addresses issues which are relevant to health, safety and welfare matters key to the project. Issues which need to be considered for inclusion in the plan include:

- how health and safety will be managed during the construction phase, including details of how information and instructions will be passed to contractors and how their activities will be co-ordinated;

- contractors' risk assessments and health and safety method statements for high risk activities;

- information about welfare arrangements sufficient to allow contractors on the project to understand how they can comply with welfare requirements;

- common arrangements (for example, on welfare, site hoardings and emergency procedures);

- how contractors, material suppliers and plant and equipment supplied for common use will be selected;

- how the views of workers and their representatives on health and safety issues associated with the project will be co-ordinated;

- information on necessary levels of health and safety training for those working on the project and arrangements for project-specific awareness training and refresher training such as toolbox talks;

- arrangements for monitoring compliance with health and safety law;

- site health and safety rules and relevant health and safety standards where appropriate, particularly where standards above the minimum statutory requirement are requested by the client;

- procedures for delivering information for the health and safety file.

The extent to which particular items need to be addressed within the plan will depend on the degree of risk associated with the project and how much coverage has been given to issues in other documents (eg contract preliminaries and contractor health and safety policies). Where the risk is low and issues are covered in the principal contractor's health and safety policy, a simple reference to the safety policy arrangements may be sufficient.

The plan should be developed as far as possible before construction work starts, and then reviewed as necessary to account for changing project circumstances. On many larger projects design may not be complete. In these cases the construction phase plan will need to address:

- [ ] the general management arrangements (for example, who will be responsible for management, how many supervisors will be needed at different stages, how information will be passed to contractors, how method statements will be agreed, etc);

- [ ] welfare arrangements and how they will be provided and maintained;

- [ ] procedures for site security;

- [ ] details of work early in the project for which information is available, explaining how it will be managed and controlled; and

- [ ] how new design information will be handled and incorporated into the plan.

What is the health and safety file?

This is a record of information for the client or end user. The planning supervisor ensures it is produced at the end of the project and is then passed to the client. It gives details of health and safety risks that will have to be managed during maintenance, repair, renovation or demolition. Contractors should pass information on these matters which becomes available during the construction phase to the planning supervisor for inclusion within the file. The client should make the file available to those who will work on any future design, construction, maintenance or demolition of the structure.

Details of how information for the file should be presented is best agreed with the client at an early stage. This will ensure that the information for the file can be gathered in a consistent manner and the file assembled and presented to the client in a way which will make it easy for the client to use. For example, some businesses prefer the file to be a separate document. Others prefer the necessary information to be incorporated within O and M manuals; in these circumstances the file will simply highlight where the necessary health and safety information can be found within the manual. Files may also be electronically produced and stored; a paper copy is not required by law.

What do the CDM Regulations require?

The client

Clients should:

- [ ] appoint a planning supervisor and principal contractor for each project;

- [ ] take reasonable steps to satisfy themselves that the planning supervisor, principal contractor, project designers and any contractors they appoint directly, are competent and adequately resourced to deal with health and safety problems associated with the project;

- [ ] pass on relevant information reasonably available to them about health and safety matters which relate to the project to those who are planning the project. If there is a health and safety file already available, relevant sections of this should be provided;

- [ ] ensure that construction work does not start unless a suitable health and safety plan has been prepared.

Clients may appoint agents to act on their behalf, but before doing so they should make reasonable enquiries to satisfy themselves that the agent is competent to fulfil the client's duties.

The designer

The term 'designer' includes everyone preparing drawings and specifications for the project. Designers include architects, structural engineers and surveyors. Before preparing any design, the designer should ensure that the client has been made aware of their own duties under the CDM Regulations.

Designers should ensure that when they design for construction work they consider foreseeable health and safety risks during construction and eventual maintenance and cleaning of the structure in the balance with other design considerations, such as aesthetics and cost. They should apply the hierarchy of risk control. This means designers need to identify the hazards inherent in carrying out the construction work and where possible alter the design to avoid them. If the hazards cannot be removed by design changes, the designer should minimise the risks and provide information about the risks that remain.

The design should describe any matters which require particular attention by a contractor. Enough information should be provided to alert contractors and others to matters which they could not be reasonably expected to know about.

The designer should also consider in the same way how the structure can be maintained and repaired safely once built. Designers should do this when they develop almost any design, including design work for projects where the appointment of a planning supervisor or principal contractor is not required by the CDM Regulations.

Examples of what designers can do to improve health and safety might include:

- designing for non-fragile roofing materials instead of fragile ones (falls through fragile materials are a major cause of fatal and serious injuries);

- avoiding the need for chasing for cable runs (a job which inevitably exposes workers to high dust and noise levels) by embedding conduit within the wall finish;

- when designing foundations in contaminated land, specifying a driven pile foundation (which does not bring contaminated material to the surface) instead of bored piles;

- avoiding concrete blocks weighing more than 20 kg (these are difficult to lift and are likely to lead to long-term back injury to blocklayers). See Construction Information Sheet No 37.[19]

Designers should co-operate with the planning supervisor and other designers on health and safety matters and supply relevant information. Where CDM applies, information can be passed via the planning supervisor; where CDM does not apply, it should be supplied as part of the design information provided to the contractors. The information should include:

- the principles of the design relevant to the health and safety of those working on the project (for example, erection sequences which must be followed to ensure stability);

- descriptions of special requirements for safe working, (for example, temporary propping of unstable structures);

☐   any special assumptions the designer has made about working practices (for example, the site will have been levelled before structural erection begins to allow the safe use of MEWPs for access for erectors).

If a firm provides any sort of design service to the client, or others, or designs temporary works, this part of the Regulations will apply to the business and it will need to know more. Detailed advice for designers can be found in *Designing for health and safety in construction*[69], *Information on site safety for designers of smaller building projects*[70] and *Managing health and safety in construction.*[71]

The planning supervisor

The planning supervisor is appointed by the client. The role of planning supervisor may be taken on by a company or an individual. The function can be discharged within the client's organisation, within the design or construction team. Alternatively it can be done by some other independent person, partnership or organisation. The role is to:

☐   co-ordinate health and safety during the design and planning phase of the project;

☐   ensure that the pre-construction stage health and safety plan for the project is produced in time for it to be provided to bidding contractors as part of the selection process;

☐   give advice about health and safety competence and resources needed for the project;

☐   ensure that written notice of the project is given to HSE (see page 20);

☐   collect information for inclusion in the health and safety file which they ensure is prepared, before passing it to the client on completion of the contract.

CDM does not require planning supervisors to visit the site or to assess the performance of the principal contractor once construction work has begun.

The principal contractor

The principal contractor is appointed by the client to plan, manage and control health and safety during the construction phase of the project.

Site work should not start until the principal contractor has developed a construction phase health and safety plan based upon information provided in the pre-construction health and safety plan (see pages 101 to 103). The plan may need to be developed during the construction phase to take account of changing conditions on site as work progresses or the design changes.

When planning the job, the principal contractor will need to identify the hazards and assess the risks of the job. To do this properly information, including method statements and risk assessments, may be needed from other contractors who will be working at the site.

When risks arise because of potential interactions between contractors (for example, site transport matters) or a number of contractors are exposed to a common risk (for example, from the site electrical distribution system), the principal contractor should take a positive role in ensuring the general principles of risk prevention and control are applied.

The principal contractor's health and safety plan should take account of the general issues in Section 1, the specific hazards and risk control measures in Section 2 and the general principles of risk assessment in this section, (see pages 94 to 95).

Contractors

These are the firms or self-employed people working at the site. They should help the principal contractor to achieve safe and healthy site conditions. They should co-operate with other contractors working on the site and provide health and safety information (including risk assessments - see pages 94 to 95) to the principal contractor.

Further information

For those who manage or work on sites where CDM applies, or those who take on the role of planning supervisor, further information is provided in *Managing health and safety in construction*[71] and *A guide to managing health and safety in construction.*[72] They explain what to do to comply with the details of the Regulations.

For those contractors who work on larger sites where CDM applies, asking about the project health and safety plan before starting work will be valuable. Employees need to be told what it says that affects them. Proposed working methods should fit in with the plan and with site rules. If they do not, tell the principal contractor.

If any of the work requires design work, even for temporary works, the Regulations will apply to the design aspect even if the Regulations do not require the appointment of a planning supervisor or a principal contractor. See *Designing for health and safety in construction*[69] for more information.

Health and safety competence

Everyone letting or subletting contracts will normally take steps to satisfy themselves that the people who will do the work are competent and resourced. CDM requires that anyone letting or subletting contracts should satisfy themselves that those who are to do the work are:

☐ competent in relevant health and safety issues; and

☐ intend to allocate adequate resources, including time, equipment and properly trained workers to do the job safely and without risks to health.

If a client is letting work, or a builder or contractor is subletting work, considering the issues in this section and Sections 1 and 2 will help them to decide on relevant questions to ask when assessing competence. Decide in advance what competences will be needed to do the work safely and without risk to health and how these can be demonstrated.

The pre-construction stage health and safety plan should act as a guide to the significant health and safety issues associated with the project.

When tendering for work, being able to answer questions on these subjects will help designers and contractors to demonstrate competence and their suitability for the job.

EMPLOYEES' DUTIES

Employees also have health and safety duties. They should:

☐   follow instructions given to them by their supervisors;

☐   co-operate with their employer on health and safety matters;

☐   follow the health and safety rules which apply to their particular job and to the site in general;

☐   use the health and safety equipment provided;

☐   report defects in equipment to their supervisor;

☐   take care of their own health and safety as well as that of their work-mates and others who might be affected by their work.

Employees should be trained to know what to do and the work should be supervised and monitored to make sure that information provided as training is relevant to the work situation and is applied effectively.

Deciding on whether or not somebody is an employee, or is self-employed, can be complex in the construction industry. It may be important to be sure of the employment status of people working on a site. It may affect who has responsibility for some aspects of health and safety and the provision of safety equipment such as boots and hats.

Remember, just because someone pays their own tax and insurance, and holds a 714 or SC60, it does not necessarily mean that they are self-employed. Deciding who is an employee depends on a range of issues. A person is more likely to be an employee when the following apply:

•   they are paid an hourly rate;

•   they are not allowed to subcontract work;

•   they can be told by another (their employer) when, how and where they are to work;

•   tools and materials are provided for them;

•   the person has not entered into a contract for a fixed sum for a package of work.

However, these tests are not always certain and legal advice may be needed to be sure of the situation. Where anyone is employed, cover will be needed under the Employers Liability (Compulsory Insurance) Act 1969. The current certificate should also be displayed by the employer.

REPORTING ACCIDENTS AND WORK-RELATED DISEASES

The Reporting of Injuries, Diseases and Dangerous Occurrences Regulations 1995 (RIDDOR) require that certain accidents, listed below, that happen on site, have to be reported to the

Incident Contact Centre,
Caerphilly Business Park,
Caerphilly CF83 3GG
website: www.riddor.gov.uk
Telephone: 0845 300 9923
Fax: 0845 300 9924
e-mail: riddor@natbrit.com

Employers must report accidents to their employees. Whoever is in control of the site must also report accidents which involve a self-employed worker. Any of the following types of accident which happen on site have to be reported:

- [ ] serious and fatal accidents must be notified without delay to HSE, normally by telephone;

- [ ] this must be followed up with a completed accident report form (F2508) within ten days;

- [ ] less serious injuries, where the injured person is unfit (or unable) to do their normal job for more than three consecutive days. A completed accident report form F2508 must be sent to HSE within ten days;

- [ ] if a dangerous occurrence happens on site, for example, a building, scaffold or falsework collapse, failure of a crane or lifting device or contact with overhead lines, it must be reported immediately, normally by telephone, to the nearest HSE office. The details must be confirmed within ten days on a completed accident report form (F2508);

- [ ] if a worker suffers from a specified disease associated with their current job, it must be reported to HSE on a completed disease report form (F2508A).

A copy of both F2508 and F2508A are included at the back of this book. These forms can be used to make reports. The forms can be photocopied for further use.

If a principal contractor has been appointed, contractors should promptly provide them with details of accidents, diseases or dangerous occurrences which are reportable or notifiable under RIDDOR.

Keeping records

A record must be kept of any reportable injury, disease or dangerous occurrence. This must include the date and method of reporting; the date, time and place of the event, personal details of those involved and a brief description of the nature of the event or disease. The record can be kept in any form preferred. For example, keep copies of completed report forms in a file.

Further details on how to report accidents and what types of accident must be reported can be found in *RIDDOR explained*.[73]

INSPECTORS AND THE LAW

Health and safety laws which apply to construction companies are usually enforced by an inspector from HSE. However, some smaller jobs inside offices, shops and similar premises are the responsibility of inspectors from the local authority. More detail of the types of job inspected by local authorities is given on page 101.

One of the jobs of health and safety inspectors is to see how well site hazards are being dealt with, especially the more serious ones which could lead to injuries or ill health. They may wish to investigate an accident or a complaint.

Inspectors do visit workplaces without notice but everyone is entitled to see their identification before letting them look around. Don't forget that they are there to give help and advice, particularly to smaller firms which may not have a lot of knowledge. When they do find problems they will try to deal with the firm in a reasonable and fair way. If anyone is not satisfied with the way they have been treated, they can take the matter up with the inspector's manager, whose name is on all letters from HSE. Any complaint about HSE inspectors will certainly be investigated, and firms will be told what is to be done to put things right if a fault is found.

Inspectors do have wide powers which include the right of entry to premises, the right to talk to employees and safety representatives and to take photographs and samples. They are entitled to workers' co-operation and answers to questions. They have the right to take written statements from anyone who can help them with their investigation.

If there is a problem, they have the right to issue a notice requiring improvements to be made, or (where a risk of serious personal injury exists), one which stops a process or the use of dangerous equipment. If a business receives an improvement or prohibition notice, it has the right to appeal to an industrial tribunal. If the business appeals against an improvement notice, the action required by the notice is suspended until the appeal is finished. The action required by a prohibition notice is not suspended pending an appeal because that could allow a serious risk to persist.

Inspectors do have the power to prosecute a business or, under certain circumstances, an individual for breaking health and safety law, but they will take their attitude and safety record into account.

If an inspector:

- **tells you to do something - you have a right, if you ask, to be given a letter** explaining what needs to be done, when and why;

- **intends to take immediate action** - for example, by issuing a prohibition notice, **you have a right to a written explanation as soon as practicable** of why this is necessary. Prohibition notices include such explanation;

- **intends to issue an improvement notice - you have a right to a written explanation of what is wrong, an outline of what needs to be done, and by when.**

When a notice is issued - you will be told in writing about your **right of appeal to an industrial tribunal,** and given a form to use to appeal. You will be told:

•   how to appeal;

•   where and within what period an appeal may be brought;

•   that an appeal may be brought on any grounds; and

•   that action required by an improvement notice is suspended while an appeal is pending.

Further details about what to do if you are not satisfied can be found in the leaflet *What to expect when a health and safety inspector calls.*[74]

4: REFERENCES AND FURTHER INFORMATION

References

1   *Safety representatives and safety committees. Approved Code of Practice and Guidance* L87 (Third edition) HSE Books 1996 ISBN 07176 1220 1

2   *Safe use of vehicles on construction sites. A guide for clients, designers, contractors, managers and workers involved with construction transport* HSG144 HSE Books 1998 ISBN 07176 1610 X

3   *Protecting the public: Your next move* HSG151 HSE Books 1997 ISBN 07176 1148 5

4   *Provision of welfare facilities at fixed construction sites* Construction Information Sheet CIS18(rev1) HSE Books 1998

5   *Provision of welfare facilities at transient construction sites* Construction Information Sheet CIS46 HSE Books 1997

6   *Safety signs and signals. The Health and Safety (Safety Signs and Signals) Regulations 1996. Guidance on Regulations* L64 HSE Books 1996 ISBN 07176 0870 0

7   *Fire safety in construction work* HSG168 HSE Books 1997 ISBN 07176 1332 1

8   Fire Protection Association/Construction Confederation *Fire prevention on construction sites. The joint code of practice on the protection from fire of construction sites and buildings undergoing renovation* 1997 (5th edition) Construction Confederation 2000
ISBN 09021 1673 91
Available from CIP, 60 Coventry Road, Sheldon, Birmingham B26 3AV.
Tel: 0121 742 0824

9   Fire Protection Association *Construction sites fire prevention checklist. A guide for insurers, surveyors and construction industry professionals* Fire Protection Association 1994
ISBN 09021 6775 8
Available from Fire Protection Association, 140 Aldersgate Street, London EC1A 4HX.
Tel: 020 7606 3757

10   *Lighting at work* HSG38 (Second edition) HSE Books 1997 ISBN 07176 1232 5

11   *Basic advice on first aid at work* Leaflet INDG347 HSE Books Books 2002 (single copy free or priced packs of 20 ISBN 0 7176 2261 4)

12   *A Guide to the Health and Safety (Consultation with Employees) Regulations 1996. Guidance on Regulations* L95 HSE Books 1996 ISBN 07176 1234 1

13   National Access & Scaffolding Confederation *The use of fall arrest equipment whilst erecting,*
      altering and dismantling scaffolding NASC guidance note NASCSG4
      NACS publications are available from CIP Ltd, FREEPOST MID20690,
      60 New Coventry Road, Sheldon, Birmingham, B26 3BR.Tel: 0121 722 8200.
      Fax: 0121 722 8201. E-mail: sales@cip-books.com

14   *Tower scaffolds* Construction Information Sheet CIS10(rev) HSE Books 1997

15   *Health and safety in roof work* HSG33 (Second edition) HSE Books 1998
      ISBN 07176 1425 5

16   *Health and safety in excavations: Be safe and shore* HSG185 HSE Books 1999
      ISBN 07176 1563 4

17   *Avoiding danger from underground services* HSG47 (Second edition) HSE Books 2000
      ISBN 07176 1744 0

18   *Safe work in confined spaces. Confined Spaces Regulations 1997. Approved Code of Practice,*
      Regulations and guidance L101 HSE Books 1997 ISBN 07176 1405 0

19   *Handling heavy building blocks* Construction Information Sheet CIS37 HSE Books 1999

20   *Manual handling. Manual Handling Operations Regulations 1992. Guidance on Regulations*
      L23 (Second edition) HSE Books 1998 ISBN 07176 2415 3

21   *Getting to grips with manual handling: A short guide for employers* Leaflet INDG143(rev1)
      HSE Books 2000 (single copy free or priced packs of 15 ISBN 0 7176 1754 8)

22   *Backs for the future: Safe manual handling in construction* HSG149 HSE Books 2000
      ISBN 07176 1122 1

23   *Manual handling: Solutions you can handle* HSG115 HSE Books 1994 ISBN 07176 0693 7

24   *Code of Practice for safe use of cranes* British Standards Institution
      BS 7121 Part 1: General: 2000
      BS 7121 Part 2: Inspection, testing and examinations: 1991

25   *Reversing vehicles* Leaflet INDG148 HSE Books 1993 (single copy free or priced packs
      of 15 ISBN 0 7176 1063 2)

26   *Rider-operated lift trucks. Operator training. Approved Code of Practice and guidance* L117
      HSE Books 1999 ISBN 07176 2455 2

27   *Workplace transport safety - guidance for employers* HSG136 HSE Books 1995
      ISBN 07176 0935 9

28   *Health risk management: A practical guide for managers in small and medium-sized enterprises*
      HSG137 HSE Books 1995 ISBN 07176 0905 7

29   *Protection of workers and the general public during the development of contaminated land*
      HSG66 HSE Books 1991 ISBN 011 885657 X

30 *A short guide to the Personal Protective Equipment at Work Regulations 1992* Leaflet INDG174 HSE Books 1995 (single copy free or priced packs of 10 ISBN 0 7176 0889 1)

31 *Personal Protective Equipment (PPE): Safety helmets* Construction Information Sheet CIS50 HSE Books 1997

32 *A step-by-step guide to COSHH assessment* HSG97 HSE Books 1993 ISBN 0 7176 1446 8

33 *Control of substances hazardous to health. The Control of Substances Hazardous to Health Regulations 2002. Approved Code of Practice and guidance* L5 (Fourth edition) HSE Books 2002 ISBN 0 7176 2534 6

34 *Health surveillance at work* HSG61 (Second edition) HSE Books 1999 ISBN 0 7176 1705 X

35 *A short guide to managing asbestos in premises* Leaflet INDG223(rev3) HSE Books 2002 (single copy free or priced packs of 10 ISBN 0 7176 2564 8)

36 *Asbestos alert for building maintenance, repair and refurbishment workers: Be aware of asbestos the hidden killer* Pocket card INDG188 HSE Books 1995 (single copy free or priced packs of 25 ISBN 0 7176 1209 0)

37 Department of the Environment *Asbestos and man-made mineral fibres in buildings. Practical guidance* 1999 ISBN 07277 2835 0 Available from Thomas Telford Ltd, 1-7 Great George St, Westminster, SW1P 3AA Tel: 020 7665 2464

38 *Working with asbestos in buildings* Leaflet INDG289 HSE Books 1999 (single copy free or priced packs of 10 ISBN 0 7176 1697 5)

39 *Work with asbestos which does not normally require a licence. Control of Asbestos at Work Regulations 2002. Approved Code of Practice and Guidance* L27 (Fourth edition) HSE Books 2002 ISBN 0 7176 2562 1

40 *Work with asbestos insulation, asbestos coating and asbestos insulating board. Control of Asbestos at Work Regulations 2002. Approved Code of Practice and Guidance* L28 (Fourth edition) HSE Books 2002 ISBN 0 7176 2563 X

41 *Working with asbestos cement* HSG189/2 HSE Books 1999 ISBN 0 7176 1667 3

42 Department of the Environment *Special Waste Regulations 1996: The controls on special waste: How they affect you* EP147 (available in England and Wales from local Environment Agency offices and in Scotland from local Scottish Environment Protection Agency offices)

43 *Asbestos dust kills - keep your mask on: Guidance for employees on wearing respiratory protective equipment for work with asbestos* Leaflet INDG255(rev1) HSE Books 1999 (single copy free or priced packs of 20 ISBN 0 7176 1696 7)

44 *Selection of suitable respiratory protective equipment for work with asbestos* Leaflet INDG288 HSE Books 1999 (single copy free or priced packs of 5 ISBN 0 7176 2456 0)

45　*Controlled asbestos stripping techniques for work requiring a licence* HSG189/1 HSE Books 1999 ISBN 0 7176 1666 5

46　*Introduction to asbestos essentials: Comprehensive guidance on working with asbestos in the building maintenance and allied trades* HSG213 HSE Books 2001 ISBN 0 7176 1901X

47　*Asbestos essentials task manual* HSG210 HSE Books 2001 ISBN 0 7176 1887 0

48　*Noise in construction. Further guidance on the Noise at Work Regulations 1989* Leaflet INDG127(rev) HSE Books 1994 (single copy free)

49　*Dust and noise in the construction process* CRR73 HSE Books 1995 ISBN 0 7176 0768 2

50　*Noise at work: Advice for employers* Leaflet INDG362 HSE Books 2002 (single copy free or priced packs of 10 ISBN 0 7176 2539 7)

51　*Hand-arm vibration syndrome: Pocket card for employees* Pocket card INDG296 HSE Books 1999 (single copy free or priced packs of 25 ISBN 0 7176 2454 4)

52　*Hand-arm vibration* HSG88 HSE Books 1994 ISBN 0 7176 0743 7

53　*Power tools: How to reduce vibration health risks - Guide for employers* Leaflet INDG338 HSE Books 2001 (single copy free or priced packs of 15 ISBN 0 7176 2008 5)

54　*Construction (Head Protection) Regulations 1989. Guidance on Regulations* L102 (Second edition) HSE Books 1998 ISBN 0 7176 1478 6

55　*Requirements for electrical installations* BS 7671: 1992

56　*Maintaining portable and transportable electrical equipment* HSG107 HSE Books 1994 ISBN 0 7176 0715 1

57　*Memorandum of guidance on the Electricity at Work Regulations 1989* HSR25 HSE Books 1989 ISBN 0 7176 1602 9

58　*Electrical safety on construction sites* HSG141 HSE Books 1995 ISBN 0 7176 1000 4

59　*Avoidance of danger from overhead electric powerlines* General Guidance Note GS6 (Third edition) HSE Books 1997 ISBN 0 7176 1348 8

60　Department of Transport *Safety at street works and road works Code of Practice* HMSO 1992 ISBN 011 551144 X

61　*Health and safety regulation: A short guide* HSC13 HSE Books 1995

62　*Five steps to risk assessment* Leaflet INDG163(rev1) HSE Books 1998 (single copy free or priced packs of 10 ISBN 0 7176 1565 0)

63　*A guide to risk assessment requirements. Common provisions in health and safety law* Leaflet INDG218 HSE Books 1996 (single copy free or priced packs of 5 ISBN 0 7176 1211 2)

64   *HSC Newsletter* - published six times a year and is available by subscription only. Subscriptions from HSE Books.

65   *Site Safe News* - published twice a year. Subscriptions from HSE Books.

66   *Need help on health and safety? Guidance for employers on when and how to get advice on health and safety* Leaflet INDG322 HSE Books 2000 (single copy free or priced packs of 10 ISBN 0 7176 1790 4)

67   *Safe use of work equipment. Provision and Use of Work Equipment Regulations 1998. Approved Code of Practice and guidance* L22 (Second edition) HSE Books 1998 0 7176 1626 6

68   *Safe use of lifting equipment. Lifting Operations and Lifting Equipment Regulations 1998. Approved Code of Practice and guidance* L113 HSE Books 1998 0 7176 1628 2

69   *Designing for health and safety in construction. A guide for designers on the Construction (Design and Management) Regulations 1994* HSE Books 1995 ISBN 0 7176 0807 7

70   *Information on site safety for designers of smaller building projects* CRR72 HSE Books 1995 ISBN 0 7176 0777 1

71   *Managing health and safety in construction: Construction (Design and Management) Regulations 1994. Approved Code of Practice and guidance* HSG224 HSE Books 2001 ISBN 0 7176 2139 1

72   *A guide to managing health and safety in construction* HSE Books 1995 ISBN 0 7176 0755 0

73   *RIDDOR explained* Leaflet HSE31(rev1) HSE Books 1999 (single copy free or priced packs of 10 ISBN 0 7176 2441 2)

74   *What to expect when a health and safety inspector calls* Leaflet HSC14 HSE Books 1998 (single copy free)

How to obtain publications

HSE priced and free publications are available by mail order from HSE Books, PO Box 1999, Sudbury, Suffolk CO10 2WA Tel: 01787 881165 Fax: 01787 313995
Website: www.hsebooks.co.uk (HSE priced publications are also available from bookshops.)

Construction Information Sheets are also available on the HSE website, www.hse.gov.uk

British Standards are available from BSI Customer Services, 389 Chiswick High Road, London W4 4AL Tel: 020 8996 9001 Fax: 020 8996 7001 Website: www.bsi-global.com

The Stationery Office (formerly HMSO) publications are available from The Publications Centre, PO Box 276, London SW8 5DT Tel: 0870 600 5522 Fax: 0870 600 5533 Website: www.clicktso.com (They are also available from bookshops.)

For information about health and safety ring HSE's Infoline Tel: 08701 545500 Fax: 02920 859260 e-mail: hseinformationservices@natbrit.com or write to HSE Information Services, Caerphilly Business Park, Caerphilly CF83 3GG. You can also visit HSE's website: www.hse.gov.uk

HSE OFFICES

Lord Cullen House, Fraser Place, **Aberdeen** AB25 3UB
Tel: 01224 252500 Fax: 01224 252525

International House, Dover Place, **Ashford** TN23 1HU
Tel: 01233 624658 Fax: 01233 634827

Priestley House, Priestley Road, **Basingstoke** RG24 9NW
Tel: 01256 404000 Fax: 01256 404100

1 Hagley Road, **Birmingham** B16 8HS
Tel: 0121 607 6200 Fax: 0121 607 6349

Inter City House, Mitchell Lane, Victoria Street, **Bristol** BS1 6AN
Tel: 01179 886000 Fax: 01179 262998

Government Buildings, Ty Glas, Llanishen, **Cardiff** CF14 5SH
Tel: 02920 263000 Fax: 02920 263120

2 Victoria Place, **Carlisle** CA1 1ER
Tel: 01228 539321 Fax: 01228 548482

3rd Floor, Darkgate Buildings, 3 Red Street, **Carmarthen** SA31 1QL
Tel: 01267 232823 Fax: 01267 223267

Wren House, Hedgerows Business Park, Colchester Road, Springfield, **Chelmsford** CM2 5PF
Tel: 01245 706200 Fax: 01245 706222

3 East Grinstead House, London Road, **East Grinstead** RH19 1RR
 Tel: 01342 334200 Fax: 01342 334222

Belford House, 59 Belford Road, **Edinburgh** EH4 3UE
Tel: 0131 247 2000 Fax: 0131 247 2121

Pegasus House, 375 West George Street, **Glasgow** G2 4LW
Tel: 0141 275 3000 Fax: 0141 275 3100

Longman House, 28 Longman Road, Longman Industrial Est., **Inverness** IV1 1SF
Tel: 01463 718101 Fax: 01463 743459

Marshalls Mill, Marshall Street, **Leeds** LS11 9YJ
Tel: 0113 283 4200 Fax: 0113 283 4296

St Dunstan's House, 201-211 Borough High Street, Southwark, **London** SE1 1GZ
Tel: 020 7556 2100 Fax: 020 7556 2200

Rose Court, 2 Southwark Bridge, **London** SE1 9HS
Tel: 020 7717 6000 Fax: 020 7717 6717

14 Cardiff Road, **Luton** LU1 1PP
Tel: 01582 444200 Fax: 01582 444320

Grove House, Skerton Road, **Manchester** M16 0RB
Tel: 0161 952 8200 Fax: 0161 952 8222

The Marches House, Midway, **Newcastle-under-Lyme** ST5 1DT
Tel: 01782 602300 Fax: 01782 602400

Arden House, Regent Centre, Gosforth, **Newcastle-upon-Tyne** NE3 3JN
Tel: 0191 202 6200 Fax: 0191 202 6300

5th Floor, Belgrave House, 1 Greyfriars, **Northampton** NN1 2BS
Tel: 01604 738300 Fax: 01604 738333

Kiln House, Pottergate, **Norwich** NR2 1DA
Tel: 01603 615711 Fax: 01603 761436

122A Thorpe Road, **Norwich** NR1 1RN
Tel: 01603 828000 Fax: 01603 828050

1st Floor, The Pearson Building, 55 Upper Parliament Street, **Nottingham** NG1 6AU Tel: 0115 971 2800 Fax: 0115 971 2802

Ballard House, West Hoe Road, **Plymouth** PL1 3BL
Tel: 01752 668481 Fax: 01752 226024

14 New Fields, Stinsford Road, Nuffield Industrial Est., **Poole** BH17 0NF
Tel: 01202 667219 Fax: 01202 667224

Marshall House, Ringway, **Preston** PR1 2HS
Tel: 0161 952 8200 Fax: 01772 836222

Edgar Allen House, 241 Glossop Road, **Sheffield** S10 2GW
Tel: 0114 291 2300 Fax: 0114 291 2379

National Agricultural Centre, **Stoneleigh** CV8 2LG
Tel: 02476 696518 Fax: 02476 696542

Haswell House, St Nicholas Street, **Worcester** WR1 1UW
Tel: 01905 723406 Fax: 01905 723045

Crown Buildings, 31 Chester Street, **Wrexham** LL13 8AN
Tel: 01978 290500 Fax: 01978 355669

HSE
Health & Safety Executive

Notification of project

Note

1. This form can be used to notify any project covered by the Construction (Design and Management) Regulations 1994 which will last longer than 30 days or 500 person days. It can also be used to provide additional details that were not available at the time of initial notification of such projects. (Any day on which construction work is carried out (including holidays and weekends) should be counted, even if the work on that day is of short duration. A person day is one individual, including supervisors and specialists, carrying out construction work for one normal working shift.)

2. The form should be completed and sent to the HSE area office covering the site where construction work is to take place. You should send it as soon as possible after the planning supervisor is appointed to the project.

3. The form can be used by contractors working for domestic clients. In this case only parts 4-8 and 11 need to be filled in.

HSE - For official use only

Client	V	PV	NV	Planning supervisor	V	PV	NV
Focus serial number				Principal contractor	V	PV	NV

1 Is this the initial notification of this project or are you providing additional information that was not previously available

Initial notification ☐   Additional notification ☐

2 Client: name, full address, postcode and telephone number *(if more than one client, please attach details on separate sheet)*

Name: Telephone number:

Address:

Postcode:

3 Planning Supervisor: name, full address, postcode and telephone number

Name: Telephone number:

Address:

Postcode:

4 Principal Contractor *(or contractor when project for a domestic client)* name, full address, postcode and telephone number

Name: Telephone number:

Address:

Postcode:

5 Address of site: where construction work is to be carried out

Address:

Postcode

F10 (rev 03.95)

6 Local Authority: name of the local government district council or island council within whose district the operations are to be carried out

```
```

7 Please give your estimates on the following: Please indicate if these estimates are original ☐ revised ☐ (tick relevant box)

a. The planned date for the commencement of the construction work

b. How long the construction work is expected to take (in weeks)

c. The maximum number of people carrying out construction work on site at any one time

d. The number of contractors expected to work on site

8 Construction work: give brief details of the type of construction work that will be carried out

```
```

9 Contractors: name, full address and postcode of those who have been chosen to work on the project (if required continue on a separate sheet) .(Note this information is only required when it is known at the time notification is first made to HSE. An update is not required)

```
```

Declaration of planning supervisor

10 I hereby declare that .... (name of organisation) has been appointed as planning supervisor for the project

Signed by or on behalf of the organisation .... (print name) ....

Date ....

Declaration of principal contractor

11 I hereby declare that .... (name of principal contractor) has been appointed as principal contractor for the project. (or contractor undertaking project for domestic client)

Signed by or on behalf of the organisation .... (print name) ....

Date ....

Health and Safety at Work etc Act 1974
The Reporting of Injuries, Diseases and Dangerous Occurrences Regulations 1995

Report of an injury or dangerous occurrence

Filling in this form
This form must be filled in by an employer or other responsible person.

Part A

About you

1 What is your full name?

2 What is your job title?

3 What is your telephone number?

About your organisation

4 What is the name of your organisation?

5 What is its address and postcode?

6 What type of work does the organisation do?

Part B

About the incident

1 On what date did the incident happen?

/ /

2 At what time did the incident happen?
(Please use the 24-hour clock eg 0600)

3 Did the incident happen at the above address?

Yes ☐ Go to question 4

No ☐ Where did the incident happen?

☐ elsewhere in your organisation – give the name, address and postcode

☐ at someone else's premises – give the name, address and postcode

☐ in a public place – give details of where it happened

If you do not know the postcode, what is the name of the local authority?

4 In which department, or where on the premises, did the incident happen?

Part C

About the injured person

If you are reporting a dangerous occurrence, go to Part F.

If more than one person was injured in the same incident, please attach the details asked for in Part C and Part D for each injured person.

1 What is their full name?

2 What is their home address and postcode?

3 What is their home phone number?

4 How old are they?

5 Are they

☐ male?

☐ female?

6 What is their job title?

7 Was the injured person (tick only one box)

☐ one of your employees?

☐ on a training scheme? Give details:

☐ on work experience?

☐ employed by someone else? Give details of the employer:

☐ self-employed and at work?

☐ a member of the public?

Part D

About the injury

1 What was the injury? (eg fracture, laceration)

2 What part of the body was injured?

F2508 (01/96)

Continued overleaf

3 Was the injury (tick the one box that applies)

☐ a fatality?

☐ a major injury or condition? (see accompanying
   notes)

☐ an injury to an employee or self-employed person
   which prevented them doing their normal work
   for more than 3 days?

☐ an injury to a member of the public which
   meant they had to be taken from the scene
   of the accident to a hospital for treatment?

4 Did the injured person (tick all the boxes that apply)

☐ become unconscious?

☐ need resuscitation?

☐ remain in hospital for more than 24 hours?

☐ none of the above.

Part E

About the kind of accident

Please tick the one box that best describes what
happened, then go to Part G.

☐ Contact with moving machinery or
   material being machined

☐ Hit by a moving, flying or falling object

☐ Hit by a moving vehicle

☐ Hit something fixed or stationary

☐ Injured while handling, lifting or carrying

☐ Slipped, tripped or fell on the same level

☐ Fell from a height
   How high was the fall?

   ┌─────────────────────┐
   │   metres   │
   └─────────────────────┘

☐ Trapped by something collapsing

☐ Drowned or asphyxiated

☐ Exposed to, or in contact with, a harmful substance

☐ Exposed to fire

☐ Exposed to an explosion

☐ Contact with electricity or an electrical discharge

☐ Injured by an animal

☐ Physically assaulted by a person

☐ Another kind of accident (describe it in Part G)

Part F

Dangerous occurrences

Enter the number of the dangerous occurrence you are
reporting. (The numbers are given in the Regulations and in
the notes which accompany this form)

┌─────────────────────┐
│   │
└─────────────────────┘

Part G

Describing what happened

Give as much detail as you can. For instance

• the name of any substance involved
• the name and type of any machine involved
• the events that led to the incident
• the part played by any people.

If it was a personal injury, give details of what the person was
doing. Describe any action that has since been taken to
prevent a similar incident. Use a separate piece of paper if
you need to.

Part H

Your signature

Signature

┌─────────────────────────────────┐
│   │
└─────────────────────────────────┘

Date

┌─────────────────────┐
│   /   /   │
└─────────────────────┘

Where to send the form
Please send it to the Enforcing Authority for the place
where it happened. If you do not know the Enforcing
Authority, send it to the nearest HSE office.

HSE
Health & Safety
Executive

Report of a case of disease

Filling in this form

This form must be filled in by an employer or other responsible person.

Part A

About you

1 What is your full name?

2 What is your job title?

3 What is your telephone number?

About your organisation

4 What is the name of your organisation?

5 What is its address and postcode?

6 Does the affected person usually work at this address?

Yes ☐ Go to question 7

No ☐ Where do they normally work?

7 What type of work does the organisation do?

Part B

About the affected person

1 What is their full name?

2 What is their date of birth?

/ /

3 What is their job title?

4 Are they

☐ male?

☐ female?

5 Is the affected person (tick one box)

☐ one of your employees?

☐ on a training scheme? Give details:

☐ on work experience?

☐ employed by someone else? Give details:

☐ other? Give details:

Part C

The disease you are reporting

1 Please give:

- the name of the disease, and the type of
  work it is associated with; or

- the name and number of the disease
  *(from Schedule 3 of the Regulations – see
  the accompanying notes).*

2 What is the date of the statement of the doctor who first
diagnosed or confirmed the disease?

/ /

3 What is the name and address of the doctor?

Part D

Describing the work that led to the disease

Please describe any work done by the affected person
which might have led to them getting the disease.

If the disease is thought to have been caused by exposure to
an agent at work *(eg a specific chemical)* please say what
that agent is.

Give any other information which is relevant.

Give your description here

Continue your description here

Part E

Your signature

Signature

Date

/ /

Where to send the form

Please send it to the Enforcing Authority for the place where
the affected person works. If you do not know the Enforcing
Authority, send it to the nearest HSE office.

CONSTRUCTION HEALTH AND SAFETY CHECKLIST

This checklist identifies some of the hazards most commonly found on construction sites. The questions it asks are intended to help you decide whether your site is a safe and healthy place to work. It is not exhaustive list. More detailed information can be found in other HSE publications.

A range of plant and equipment (eg scaffolds, cranes, hoists, electrical equipment and excavations) needs to be inspected on a regular basis by a competent person to ensure safety. Records of inspection may also be required. Further details on these particular inspections are given at the back of the report form also included in this section.

Regular inspection is important but it is also essential that when defects are identified by the inspection, or reported by people using the equipment, either the defects are remedied immediately or work is stopped until necessary repairs are completed.

Access on site

☐ Can everyone get to their place of work safely - and work there safely?

☐ Are access routes in good condition and clearly signposted?

☐ Are edges which people could fall from provided with double guard rails or other suitable edge protection?

☐ Are holes protected with clearly marked and fixed covers to prevent falls?

☐ Are temporary structures stable, adequately braced and not overloaded?

☐ Will permanent structures remain stable during any refurbishment or demolition work?

☐ Is the site tidy, and are materials stored safely?

☐ Is lighting adequate, especially when work is being carried on after dark outside or inside buildings?

Scaffolds

☐ Are scaffolds erected, altered and dismantled by competent people?

☐ Are all uprights provided with base plates (and, where necessary, timber sole plates)?

☐ Are all uprights, ledgers, braces and struts in position?

☐ Is the scaffold secured to the building or structure in enough places to prevent collapse?

 ☐ Are there double guard rails and toe boards, or other suitable protection, at every edge, to prevent falling?

☐ Are additional brick guards provided to prevent materials falling from scaffolds?

☐ Are the working platforms fully boarded and are the boards arranged to avoid tipping or tripping?

☐ Are there effective barriers or warning notices in place to stop people using an incomplete scaffold, eg where working platforms are not fully boarded?

☐ Is the scaffold strong enough to carry the weight of materials stored on it and are these evenly distributed?

☐ Are scaffolds being properly maintained?

☐ Does a competent person inspect the scaffold regularly, eg at least once a week; and always after it has been altered or damaged and following extreme weather?

☐ Are the results of inspections recorded?

☐ Have proprietary tower scaffolds been erected and are they being used in accordance with suppliers' instructions?

☐ Have the wheels of tower scaffolds been locked when in use and are the platforms empty when they are moved?

Ladders

☐ Are ladders the right way to the job? Don't work from a ladder if there is a better way!

☐ Are they in good condition?

☐ Do ladders rest against a solid surface and not on fragile or insecure materials?

☐ Are they secured to prevent them slipping sideways or outwards?

☐ Do ladders rise a sufficient height above their landing place? If not, are other hand-holds available?

☐ Are the ladders positioned so that users do not have to overstretch?

Roof work

☐ Is there edge protection to stop people or materials falling?

☐ During industrial roofing, have nets been provided to stop people falling from the leading edge of the roof and from partially fixed sheets?

☐ Where nets are used, have they been hung safely?

☐ Have you identified fragile materials such as cement sheets and roof lights?

☐ Have you taken precautions to stop people falling through fragile materials when working on the roof eg by providing barriers, covers or working platforms?

☐ Are people kept away from the area below the roof work? If this is not possible, have additional precautions been taken to stop debris falling onto them?

Excavations

☐ Is there adequate support for the excavation, or has it been sloped or battered back to a safe angle?

☐ Is there a safe method used for putting in the support, without people working in an unsupported trench?

☐ Is there safe access into the excavation, eg a sufficiently long, secured ladder?

☐ Are there barriers or other protection to stop people and vehicles falling in?

☐ Are properly secured stop blocks provided to prevent tipping vehicles falling in?

☐ Could the excavation affect the stability of neighbouring structures or services?

☐ Are materials, spoil and plant stored away from the edge of the excavation to reduce the chance of a collapse?

☐ Is the excavation regularly inspected by a competent person?

Manual handling

☐ Are there heavy materials such as roof trusses, concrete lintels, kerbstones or bagged products which could cause problems if they have to be moved by hand?

If so, can you:

· choose lighter materials?

· use wheelbarrows, hoists, telehandlers, and other plant or equipment so that manual lifting of heavy objects is kept to a minimum?

· order materials such as cement and aggregates in 25 kg bags?

· avoid the repetitive laying of heavy building blocks weighing more than 20 kg?

☐ Have people been instructed and trained how to lift safely?

Traffic, vehicles and plant

☐ Are vehicles and pedestrians kept apart?
If not, do you:
· separate them as much as you can and use barriers?
· tell people about the problem, and what to do about it?
· display warning signs?

☐ Is there adequate clearance around slewing vehicles?

☐ Can reversing be avoided, eg by using a one-way system or, if not, are properly trained signallers used?

☐ Are vehicles and plant properly maintained eg do the steering lights, handbrake and footbrake work properly?

☐ Have drivers received proper training and are they competent for the vehicles or plant they are operating?

☐ Are loads properly secured?

☐ Have you made sure that passengers are only carried on vehicles designed to carry them?

☐ Have you made sure that plant and vehicles are not used on dangerous slopes?

Tools and machinery

☐ Are the right tools or machinery being used for the job?

☐ Are all dangerous parts guarded, eg gears, chains drives, projecting engine shafts?

☐ Are guards secured and in good repair?

☐ Are tools and machinery maintained in good repair and are all safety devices operating correctly?

☐ Are all operators trained and competent?

Powered access equipment

☐ Has the equipment been installed by a competent person?

☐ Are the operators trained and competent?

☐ Is the safe working load clearly marked?

☐ Is the equipment inspected by a competent person?

☐ Does the working platform of the powered access equipment have adequate, secure guard rails and toe boards or other barriers to prevent people and materials falling off?

☐ Have precautions been taken to prevent people being struck by:
- the moving platform;
- projections from the building; or
- falling materials?

Hoists

☐ Has the equipment been installed by a competent person?

☐ Are the operators trained and competent?

- [ ] Is the rated capacity clearly marked?

- [ ] Are the hoists inspected by a competent person?

- [ ] Does the hoist have a current report of thorough examination and a record of inspection?

- [ ] Is there a suitable base enclosure to prevent people from being struck by any moving part of the hoist?

- [ ] Are the landing gates kept shut except when the platform is at the landing?

- [ ] Are controls arranged so that the hoist can be operated from one position only?

Cranes

- [ ] Is the crane suitable for the job?

- [ ] Has the lift been properly planned?

- [ ] Is the crane on a firm level base; are the riggers properly set?

- [ ] Are the crane driver and signaller trained and competent?

- [ ] Is the load secure?

- [ ] Has the signaller/slinger been trained to give signals and to attach loads correctly?

- [ ] Have you made arrangements to make sure the driver can see the load or has a signaller been provided to help?

- [ ] Are people stopped from walking or working beneath a raised load?

- [ ] Does the crane have a current report of through examination and record of inspection?

Fires and emergencies

General

- [ ] Are there emergency procedures eg for evacuating the site in case of fire, or for rescue from a confined space?

- [ ] Do people on site know what the procedures are?

- [ ] Is there a means of raising the alarm, and does it work?

- [ ] Is there a way to contact the emergency services from site?

- [ ] Are there adequate escape routes and are these kept clear?

- [ ] Is there adequate first-aid provision?

Fire

☐ Is the quantity of flammable materials, liquids and gases on site kept to a minimum?

☐ Are they properly stored?

☐ Are suitable containers used for flammable liquids?

☐ Are flammable gas cylinders returned to a ventilated store at the end of the shift?

☐ Are smoking and other ignition sources banned in areas where gases or flammable liquids are stored or used?

☐ Are gas cylinders, associated hoses and equipment properly maintained and in good condition?

☐ When gas cylinders are not in use, are the valves fully closed?

☐ Is flammable and combustible waste removed regularly and stored in suitable bins or skips?

☐ Are suitable fire extinguishers provided?

Hazardous substances

☐ Have you identified all harmful substances and materials, such as asbestos, lead, solvents, paints, cement and dust?

☐ Have you checked whether a licensed contractor is needed to deal with asbestos on site? (Most work with asbestos requires a licence, although you can do some very limited work with material which contain asbestos without one.)

☐ Have you identified and put into place precautions to prevent or control exposure to hazardous substances, by:
   • doing the work in a different way, to remove the risk entirely;
   • using a less hazardous material; or
   • using tools fitted with dust extraction?

☐ Have workers had information and training so they know what the risks are from the hazardous substances used and produced on site, and what they need to do to avoid the risks?

☐ Have you got procedures to prevent contact with wet cement (as this can cause both dermatitis and cement burns)?

☐ Have you arranged health surveillance for people using certain hazardous substances (eg lead)?

Confined spaces

☐ Do you work in confined spaces where there may be an inadequate supply of oxygen or the presence of poisonous or flammable gas? If so, have you taken all necessary precautions?

☐ Confined spaces include tanks, sewers and manholes: they do not have to look dirty to be dangerous!

Noise

☐ Have workers had information and training so they know what the risks are from noise on site, and what they need to do to avoid those risks?

☐ Have you identified and assessed workers' exposure to noise?

☐ Can the noise be reduced by using different working methods or selecting quieter plant eg by fitting breakers and other plant or machinery with silencers?

☐ Are people not involved in the work kept away from the source of the noise?

☐ Is suitable hearing protection provided and worn in noisy areas?

☐ Have hearing protection zones been marked?

☐ Have you arranged health surveillance for people exposed to high levels of noise?

Hand-arm vibration

☐ Have workers had information and training so they know what the risks are from hand-arm vibration (HAV) on site, and what they need to do to avoid those risks?

☐ Have you identified and assessed risks to workers from prolonged use of vibrating tools such as concrete breakers, angle grinders or hammer drills?

☐ Has exposure to HAV been reduced as much as possible by selecting suitable work methods and plant?

☐ Are reduced-vibration tools used whenever possible?

☐ Have vibrating tools been properly maintained?

☐ Have you arranged health surveillance for people exposed to high levels of hand-arm vibration, especially when exposed for long periods?

Welfare

☐ Are toilets readily available and are they kept clean and properly lit?

☐ Are there washbasins, hot and cold (or warm) running water, soap and towels?

☐ Are the washbasins large enough to wash up to the elbow and are they kept clean?

☐ Is there somewhere to change, dry and store clothing?

☐ Are drinking water and cups provided?

☐ Is there a place where workers can sit, make hot drinks and prepare food?

☐ Can everyone who needs to use them get to the welfare facilities easily and safely?

Electricity and other services

☐ Have all necessary services been provided on site before work begins and have you also identified existing services present on site (eg electric cables or gas mains) and taken effective steps, if necessary, to prevent danger from them?

☐ Are you using low voltage for tools and equipment eg battery-operated tools or low voltage systems?

☐ Where mains voltage has to be used, are trip devices, eg residual current devices (RCDs), provided for all equipment?

☐ Are RCDs checked daily by users and properly maintained?

☐ Are cables and leads protected from damage?

☐ Are all connections to the system properly made and are suitable plugs used?

☐ Are tools and equipment checked by users, visually examined on site and regularly inspected and tested by a competent person?

☐ Where there are overhead lines, has the electricity supply been turned off, or have other precautions been taken, such as providing 'goal posts' or taped markers?

☐ Have hidden electricity cables and other services been located (eg with a locator and plans) and marked, and have you taken precautions for safe working?

Protecting the public

☐ Is the work fenced off from the public?

☐ Are roadworks barriered off and lit?

☐ Are the public protected from falling material?

☐ When work has stopped for the day:
  • is the boundary secure and undamaged?
  • are all ladders removed or their rungs boarded so that they cannot be used?
  • are excavations and openings securely covered or fenced off?
  • is all plant immobilised to prevent unauthorised use?
  • are bricks and materials safely stacked?
  • are flammable or dangerous substances locked away in secure storage places?

Construction (Health, Safety and Welfare) Regulations 1996

INSPECTION REPORT

Report of results of every inspection made in pursuance of regulation 29(1)

1. Name and address of person for whom inspection was carried out.

2. Site address

3. Date and time of inspection.

4. Location and description of workplace (including any plant, equipment or materials) inspected.

5. Matters which give rise to any health and safety risks.

6. Can work be carried out safely?

    Y / N

7. If not, name of person informed.

8. Details of any other action taken as a result of matters identified in 5 above.

9. Details of any further action considered necessary.

10. Name and position of person making the report.

11. Date report handed over.

Construction (Health, Safety and Welfare) Regulations 1996

INSPECTION REPORTS: NOTES

Place of work requiring inspection	Timing and frequency of inspection					
	Before being used for the first time.	After substantial addition, dismantling or alteration.	After any event likely to have affected its strength or stability.	At regular intervals not exceeding 7 days.	Before work at the start of every shift	After accidental fall of rock, earth or any material.
Any working platform or part thereof or any personal suspension equipment.	✓	✓	✓	✓		
Excavations which are supported in pursuit of paragraphs (1), (2) or (3) of regulation 12.			✓		✓	
Cofferdams and caissons.			✓		✓	✓

NOTES

General

1. The inspection report should be completed before the end of the relevant working period.
2. The person who prepares the report should, within 24 hours, provide either the report or a copy to the person on whose behalf the inspection was carried out.
3. The report should be kept on site until work is complete. It should be retained for three months at an office of the person for whom the inspection was carried out.

Working platforms only

1. An inspection is only required where a person is liable to fall more than 2 metres from a place of work.
2. Any employer or any other person who controls the activities of persons using a scaffold shall ensure that it is stable and of sound construction and that the relevant safeguards are in place before his employees or persons under his control first use the scaffold.
3. No report is required following the inspection of any mobile tower scaffold which remains in the same place for less than 7 days.
4. Where an inspection of a working platform or part thereof or any personal suspension equipment is carried out:
   i.   before it is taken into use for the first time; or
   ii.   after any substantial addition, dismantling or other alteration;
   not more than one report is required for any 24 hour period.

Excavations only

1. The duties to inspect and prepare a report apply only to any excavation which needs to be supported to prevent any person being trapped or buried by an accidental collapse, fall or dislodgement of material from its sides, roof or area adjacent to it. Although an excavation must be inspected at the start of every shift, only one report of such inspections is required every 7 days. Reports must be completed for all inspections carried out during this period for other purposes, e.g. after accidental fall of material.

Checklist of typical scaffolding faults

Footings	Standards	Ledgers	Bracing	Putlogs and transoms	Couplings	Bridles	Ties	Boarding	Guard-rails and toe-boards	Ladders
Soft and uneven	Not plumb	Not level	Some missing	Wrongly spaced	Wrong fitting	Wrong spacing	Some missing	Bad boards	Wrong height	Damaged
No base plates	Jointed at same height	Joints in same bay	Loose	Loose	Loose	Wrong couplings	Loose	Trap boards	Loose	Insufficient length
No sole plates	Wrong spacing	Loose	Wrong fittings	Wrongly supported	Damaged	No check couplers	Not enough	Incomplete	Some missing	Not tied
Undermined	Damaged	Damaged	-	-	No check couplers	-	-	Insufficient supports	-	-

Questionnaire

HEALTH AND SAFETY IN CONSTRUCTION

To help us assess this publication, will you please complete and return this questionnaire to the address overleaf. Postage is free.

We may wish to contact a sample of respondents with a fuller survey in future. If you do not wish to be contacted again please tick this box ☐

Mr, Mrs, Ms, Dr, Other _____ Initials _____ Surname _____

Position _____

Name of business _____

Address _____

_____

Postcode _____ Telephone _____ Fax _____

Size of business? (Number of employees)

Fewer than 5 ☐ 5 - 10 ☐ 10 - 20 ☐ 20 - 50 ☐ 50 - 100 ☐ 100 - 250 ☐ Over 250 ☐ Self-employed ☐

What is your main activity?

General building ☐		*Roofing* ☐		*Painting* ☐	
Joinery ☐		*Bricklaying* ☐		*Plumbing* ☐	
Other (please specify) ☐					

How did you hear about this publication?

Advertisement ☐		*HSE Inspector* ☐		*Trade Association* ☐	
HSC Newsletter/News Bulletin ☐		*HSE Catalogue* ☐		*Mailshot* ☐	
Local authority ☐		*Informal business contact* ☐		*Other (please specify)* ☐	

Did you find the publication:

clear and straightforward?			*difficult to understand?*
1	2	3	4

Was the publication:

too technical?			*not technical enough?*
1	2	3	4

Was the publication:

well presented?			*poorly presented?*
1	2	3	4

Do you feel that the publication represents:

very good value?			*poor value for money?*
1	2	3	4

Was the publication helpful to you in identifying the health and safety risks associated with the work you do:

very useful			*not useful?*
1	2	3	4

Was the advice in the publication useful to you in identifying ways of controlling health and safety risks associated with your work:

very useful			*not useful?*
1	2	3	4

Did the publication help you to understand your responsibilities for health and safety:

very well	*well*	*a little*	*not at all?*
1	2	3	4

How much of the advice was relevant to the work you do:

all	*most*	*some*	*none?*
1	2	3	4

Have you bought any of the titles in the CDM guidance package? Y N

Any other comments _____

Thank you for taking the time to answer these questions

FIRST FOLD

643

THIRD FOLD

Tuck A into B to form envelope
Please do not staple or glue

A

Health and Safety Executive
Room 303, Daniel House
Stanley Precinct
BOOTLE
Merseyside L20 3QY

BUSINESS REPLY SERVICE
Licence No. LV 5189

SECOND FOLD

B

Printed and published by the Health and Safety Executive
C150   Reprinted 4/04